How to

GET FIT FOR SPORT

a step-by-step guide

Author: Liz French

Technical consultant:
Tim Newenham
National Athletics
Event Coach
Lecturer for National
Coaching Foundation

JARROLD

Other titles in this series are:

TENNIS
SQUASH
BADMINTON
CROQUET
BOWLS
TABLE TENNIS
SWIMMING
GOLF
WINDSURFING
SNOOKER
DINGHY SAILING

How to get FIT FOR SPORT
ISBN 0-7117-0506-2
First published in Great Britain, 1990

Illustrations by Malcolm Ryan

Designed and produced by
Parke Sutton Limited, Norwich
for Jarrold Publishing, Norwich

Contents

Introduction

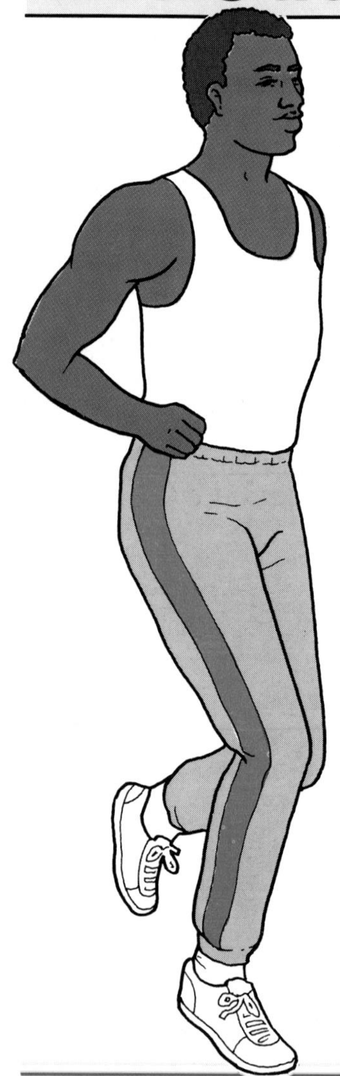

Sport today is accessible to everyone, with an enormous range of activities to choose from. Participating in sport can be enjoyed at all levels and by all age groups – and it is never too late to start. Whether you aspire to the top levels of competition or play your sport purely for the personal pleasure and challenge, it is important to remember that most sport does not actually get you fit – you have to get fit for sport. All top sportsmen and women train hard to build and maintain high levels of general fitness as well as to develop the skills specific to their own sport. The same principles apply whatever your levels of achievement and experience.

'How to get fit for sport' is designed to help you work out a fitness programme based on your own specific needs. It begins with a basic explanation of what fitness is and how to measure your own levels of fitness, then continues with detailed, practical advice on how to get started and how to build up to maximum fitness levels. The book is intended both for those already committed to regular participation in a specific sport and for those interested in fitness for its own sake.

Many exercises and routines are included which can be performed at home with no special equipment. There are also sections explaining the use of weight-training machines of the type found in sports centres, recreation centres and fitness centres everywhere. Weight training is increasingly and very effectively used by both men and women for all kinds of fitness training and does not necessarily mean developing bulging biceps! This book will tell you what to expect from your visits to the gym and help you get the most from a weight-training programme. It is also well worth joining a good, reputable club where you will receive expert instruction in a well-equipped, safe environment.

Whatever your chosen sport, becoming – and staying – fit will have far-reaching effects not just on your sports performance but on your life in general. You will have more vitality and will look and feel better. You will find it easier to relax. And you will have more than enough energy to meet the everyday demands of your work and leisure hours. Have fun!

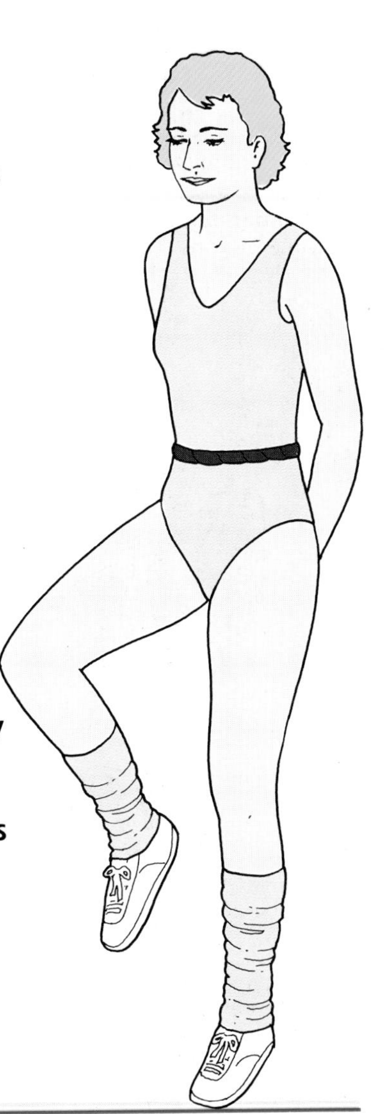

Dress

The basic requirement for fitness training is comfortable, loose clothing. Tracksuits, shorts and top, leotard and tights . . . all are suitable options.

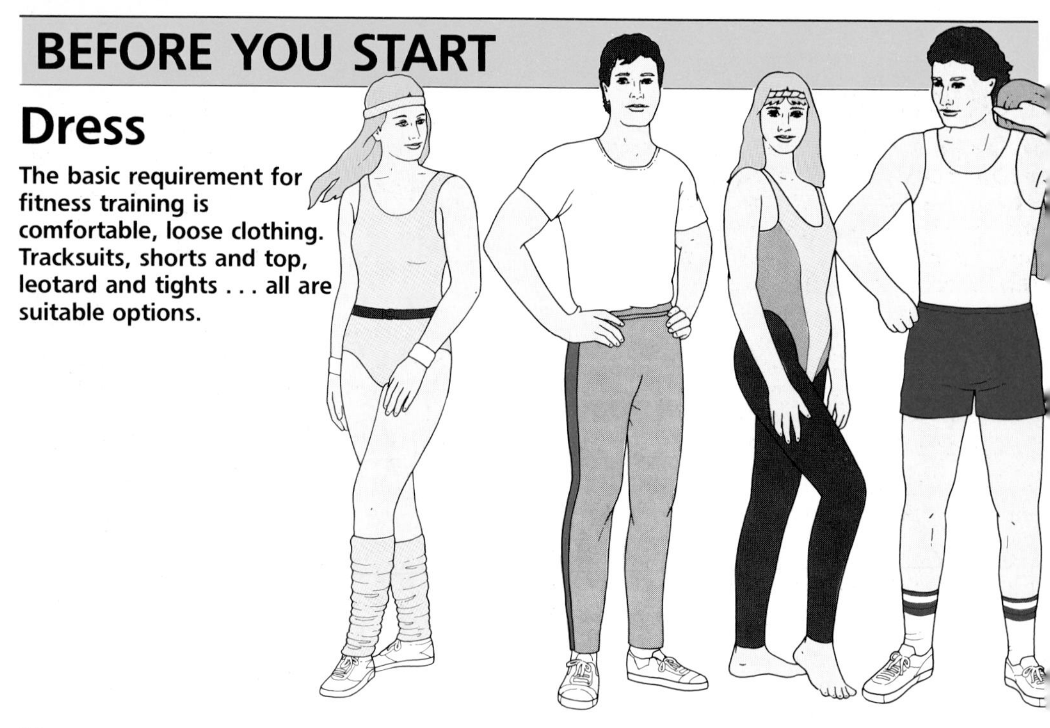

Shoes

- For weight training (see pages 32-47), any well-fitting, non-slip, lightweight training shoe or plimsoll will do.
- For any kind of activity involving running or jumping you really need a good pair of properly cushioned running shoes. These are vital for protecting your feet, joints and back from strain and injury.
- For some aerobic and stretching exercises, particularly those done at home, you may prefer bare feet.

When choosing training shoes, it can be a good idea to buy a size (of half-size) larger than usual; your feet will tend to spread slightly when you exercise and you may be wearing thick socks.

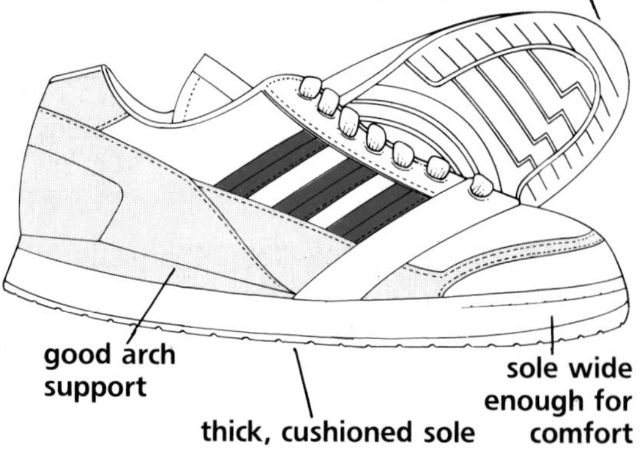

Equipment

In this book you will find many exercises which require no special equipment. The sections on weight training (see pages 32-47) are based on machines and free weights of the type found in sports and recreation centres, clubs and gyms everywhere.

Weight training equipment may vary, but the basic exercise techniques will be the same. Always follow the advice of the instructor at your gym or centre. You can buy weight-training equipment for use at home, but good examples are expensive.

Free weights, including dumb-bells and weighted ankle and wrist straps are useful if you do not have easy access to a properly equipped and supervised gym, but make sure you follow the maker's or retailer's instructions carefully to avoid strains and injuries.

What is Fitness?

Fitness is a combination of elements, each of which contributes to the whole state. These components are sometimes known as the five S's:

Stamina

Stamina, or endurance, means being able to keep going at physical work or exercise. It refers both to general body stamina and the capacity of a particular muscle or group of muscles to work continuously. The kind of energetic, continuous exercise needed to increase your stamina is called 'aerobic' because it requires extra oxygen and makes you slightly out of breath.

Suppleness

Suppleness, or flexibility, refers to the range of movement in a joint. It means being able to bend, twist and stretch freely through a whole range of movement.

Strength

Strength is measured by how much force a muscle or group of muscles can generate for lifting, pushing or pulling against a resistance. Your strength will vary for different parts of your body and depends on the quality and size of your muscles.

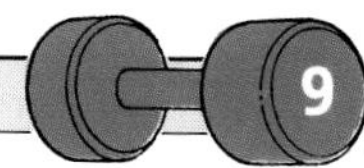

Speed

This refers to how fast your body can move, and also to how quickly your brain and reflexes respond to a stimulus to move.

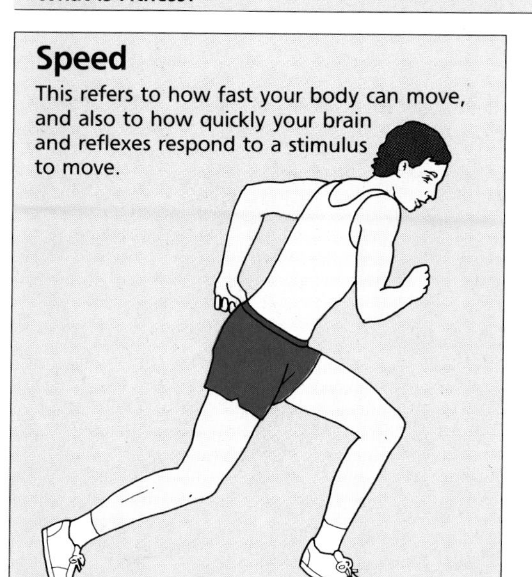

Skill

Particular sports require particular skills. Developing a specific skill can be a focus for your fitness training – but it *must* be built on a base of good all-round fitness.

Other factors contributing to over-all fitness are: • sleep and relaxation • good diet • correct weight

How Fit are You?

To get an accurate, overall picture of how fit you are, go to a health centre, club or gym which offers comprehensive fitness testing. They will offer a combination of tests to assess your stamina, suppleness, strength and speed.

Three basic checks you can do yourself will, however, give a rough idea of your fitness level:

1 Your pulse before and after exercise

Place two fingers of one hand across the opposite wrist and count the number of beats over a 30 second period. Then multiply by two. This is your pulse at rest, and it should be somewhere between 50 and 85 beats per minute.

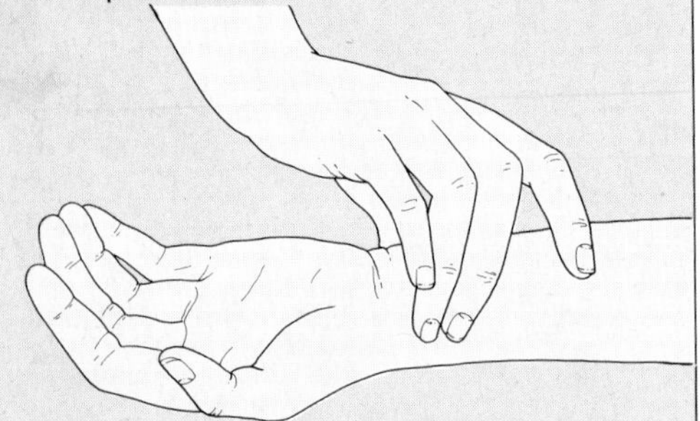

Now do three minutes of fairly vigorous exercise – say, running on the spot, raising your knees progressively higher, or stepping on and off a low bench. Take your pulse again, within five seconds of stopping the activity. It should have risen by less than 50% of your resting rate.

Finally, sit down and see how long it takes for your pulse to return to its resting rate. Under a minute? Good. More than three minutes? You need to start your fitness training very gradually (see page 15).

2 Your balance

Stand with feet together and arms clasped behind your back. Now lift one knee and close your eyes. Can you stand like this for 15 seconds or more? If not, there could be a problem with your nerves, your muscles or the balancing mechanism in your ear.

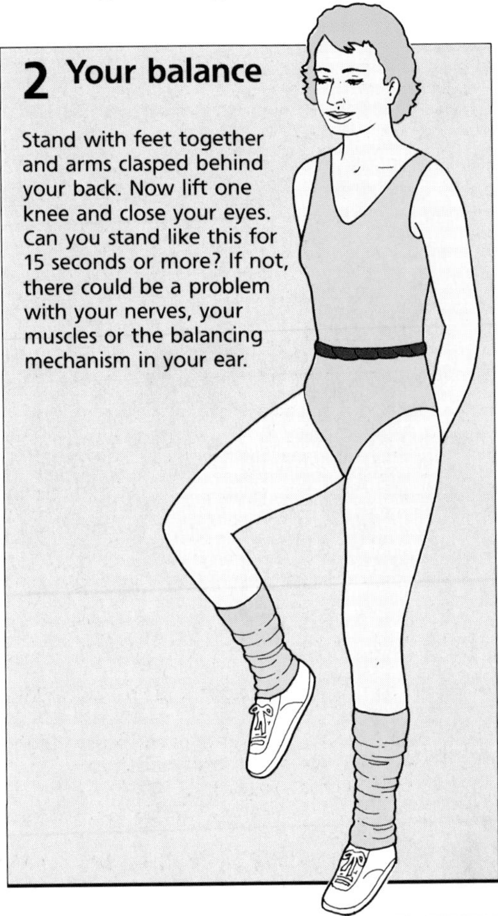

3 Your weight

Weight is a good general indicator of fitness, because a high proportion of fat can make your health suffer. On the chart below, take a line across from your height and a line up from your weight and check your rating where the lines cross. You should take into account whether you have a large, medium or small bone frame and aim for the upper, middle or lower weight range for your height accordingly. If you DO need to lose weight, you will need a combination of better diet (see page 14) and exercise. Crash diets are NOT recommended.

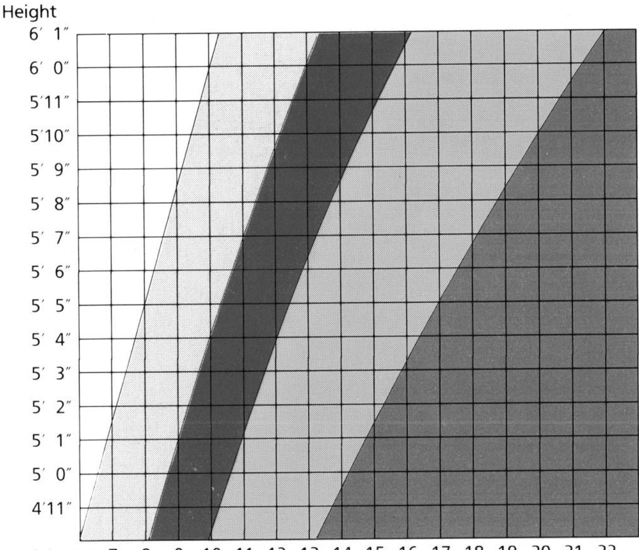

- **You are underweight and could do with gaining a few pounds.**
- **You are the ideal weight for your height.**
- **You are starting to get fat and should take care to eat sensibly (see page 14).**
- **You need to lose weight because your health could be in danger.**
- **You are severely overweight and should see your doctor.**

Safety sense

You should consult your doctor before starting any fitness programme if you:

- **Have had a major illness or accident within the last five years**
- **Have ever suffered from chest pains or unusual fluctuations in your heart rate**
- **Suffer from asthma or bronchitis**
- **Have ever been diagnosed as diabetic**
- **Suffer from high blood pressure**
- **Have periods of faintness or dizziness**
- **Sometimes get breathless without exercise**
- **Are prone to migraines or headaches**
- **Are taking prescribed drugs**
- **Are pregnant**
- **Are over 35 and have not exercised before**
- **Have any doubts at all about your health**

Your Body's Major Muscles

Your level of fitness depends to a large extent on how efficiently your muscles perform. The two diagrams on this page show you the major muscle groups you will be working on during your fitness programme. Remember that the heart is a muscle, too, and needs to be exercised.

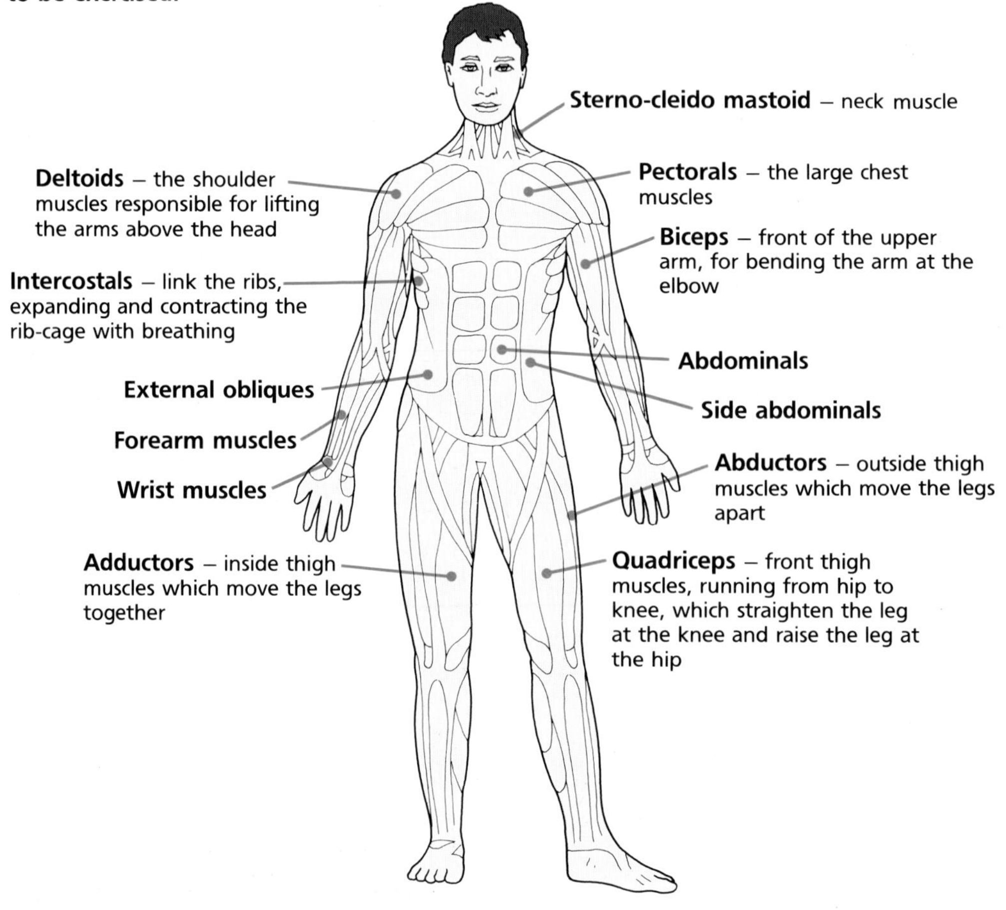

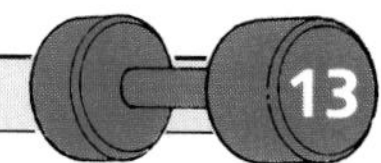

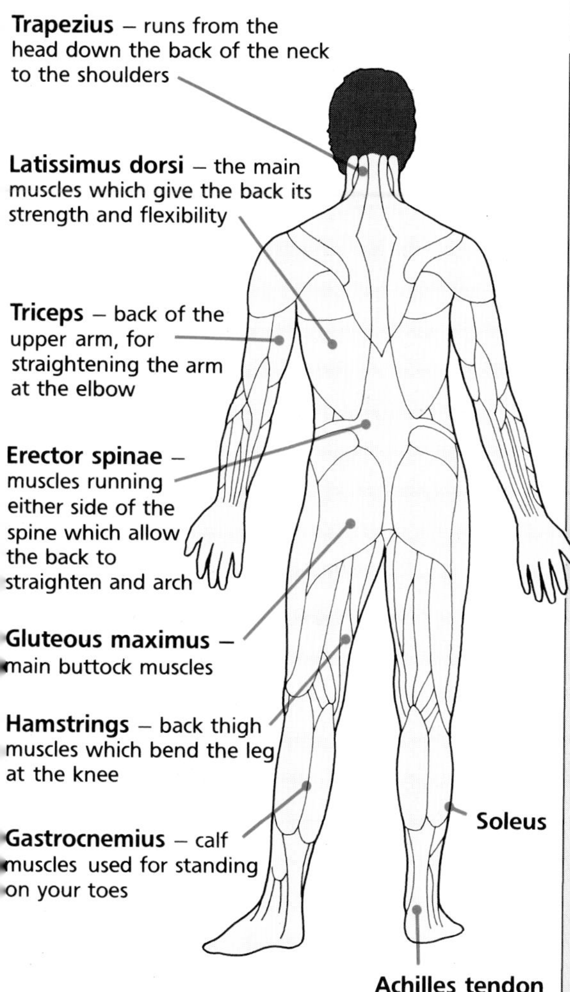

How Muscles Work

Muscles are arranged in pairs

So, for example, you use one muscle group to bend a limb and another to straighten it.

Muscles are made up of two types of fibre

- Slow-twitch type for endurance. These move slowly but don't tire easily. They are used first when overcoming resistance.
- Fast-twitch type for sudden, explosive actions. These move more quickly but tire easily. They are used if the slow-twitch type have not overcome the resistance.

Muscles need energy

The immediate source of energy in the muscles is a compound called ATP which your body produces in different ways according to the type of activity you are engaged in.

Why muscles feel tired

The fatigue felt in your muscles during prolonged exercise is caused by a build-up of a waste product called lactic acid. This in turn requires oxygen to carry it away, which is one reason why you breathe faster and your heart rate goes up when you are exercising. It can take some time to recover the 'oxygen debt': this is why you continue to pant and your heart beats faster for some minutes after you stop the activity. If too much excess lactic acid builds up, you may get cramp (painful, spasmodic contraction of muscles).

What is happening?

If you are fit:

- you take longer to get out of breath
- muscles tire less easily • recovery time is shorter

If you are unfit:

- you get out of breath more quickly
- muscles tire more easily • recovery time is longer

Diet

A varied and balanced diet is a basic requirement for fitness. You can find detailed information on diet and nutrition – some of it confusing and unnecessarily complicated – in numerous books and magazines. But the basic rules are simple:

• go for a balanced diet • don't over-eat • limit your fat intake

Eat MORE high-fibre foods:
wholemeal bread and cereals
beans and pulses
raw fruit and vegetables

Eat LESS: sugary foods and drinks
fatty foods
salt

If you think your diet could be better, here are some simple ways to adapt it:

- Switch from full-fat milk to skimmed or semi-skimmed
- Use low-fat spread instead of butter
- Eat less red meat and choose less-fatty cuts
- Choose white meat and fish
- Choose low-fat cheeses and yogurts
- Buy canned fruit that is in natural juice rather than syrup
- Grill rather than fry and, if you must fry, use the stir-fry method and very little oil

The fatty facts

Food contains two main kinds of fat. Most experts agree that it is healthier to reduce fat intake overall, and to substitute polyunsaturated fats for the more dangerous saturated fats:

SATURATED	POLYUNSATURATED
Contributes to the risk of heart disease	Contains essential fatty acids like linoleic acid, vital for health
Raises blood cholesterol levels	Helps to lower blood cholesterol
High levels found in butter, lard, most meat and meat products such as sausages and paté	Found naturally in some nuts and seeds, such as sunflower seeds, and in oily fish like mackerel

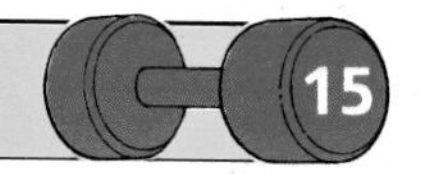

Gently at First

If your body is unused to exercise, and particularly if you are older, it is essential that you start gently, exercising for short periods of ten or fifteen minutes, three or four times a week and gradually building up to a more rigorous routine. The object should be to enjoy yourself!

The right way to exercise

Exercise must be:

- REGULAR – three times a week is fine.
- BALANCED – aim to build up all the elements outlined on pages 8 and 9, even if your ultimate aim is to increase your skill in a particular sport.
- SAFE – always use a warm-up routine before you start and warm-down afterwards (see page 17). Exercise within your training heart rate (see page 17).

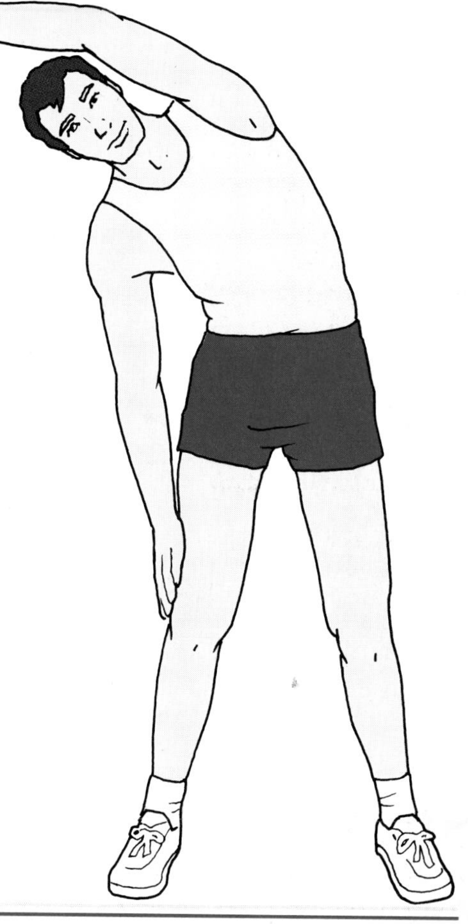

The wrong way to exercise

Aches, strains, cramps, sprains, pulled muscles, torn ligaments and even breakages can all occur as a direct result of sport and exercise. Most injuries are caused by:

- SUDDEN IMPACT, particularly if there has been inadequate warm-up
- OVERUSE AND POOR TECHNIQUE

The message is obvious:

- Take it carefully – don't try to do too much too soon
- Stop if you feel any pain
- Drink water often, before and during exercise – dehydration is a likely cause of cramp
- Drink BEFORE you feel thirsty; a little and often is the rule

A Training Session

To gain maximum benefit from your training sessions, you need to plan them carefully according to some basic principles:

Intensity: how hard?

For your level of fitness actually to increase, your body has to work harder than it does normally: this is known as the overload factor. Below a certain stress level, you will only be maintaining your current fitness. The intensity you need to work at will vary, but you can use your training heart rate (see opposite) as a guide.

Duration: how long?

The amount of time you need to spend at each training session to gain maximum benefit from it will again vary, but as a general guide, if you have not exercised regularly before, your sessions could be 20 minutes long at first, including five minutes warm-up (see opposite). Build up gradually from this as your fitness levels improve.

Frequency: how often?

After a particular body system has been overloaded, it needs time to recover. In the early stages, three sessions a week are fine, with rest days in between. If you want to exercise every day, it is sensible to alternate so that full work-outs are followed with days when you perhaps run, swim or cycle.

Progress: how fast?

If you are starting from scratch, your initial progress may be quite startling. Don't be discouraged when these dramatic results don't continue at the same rate. You should, in fact, aim to make steady long-term progress. Keeping a record of how your training is progressing is highly recommended (see particularly the section on weight training, pages 32-47).

A typical training session for a fairly fit person might be as follows:

Warm-up **10 minutes**
Main exercise **45 minutes**
Warm-down **5 minutes**

Your main exercise should be structured to balance the various elements – stamina, suppleness, strength and speed. You will find some exercises and routines for each of these in the following pages (later you can build on the specific skills required for your particular sport, if appropriate). You might achieve the balance by concentrating on, say, strength and suppleness at one day's session and alternating with a bout of running or other aerobic training the next.

Warm-up and Warm-down

Warm-up

Before you start an exercise session, it is essential to prepare your muscles and joints for what is to follow. This means warming up your muscles gradually and progressively, increasing your pulse rate to your training rate (see below) and making your lungs work gradually harder. That way your body will be better able to cope with the increased demand for oxygen created by exercise. The importance of the warm-up routine cannot be over-emphasised. If you neglect it, you are likely to suffer the consequences with injuries.

- Warm up for at least five minutes, and preferably ten or fifteen.
- Don't pause for long between warming up and starting your exercise.
- Start with a whole-body warm-up such as light running, skipping or using an exercise bike.
- Then continue with gentle stretching and loosening exercises, using all the major muscle groups and concentrating particularly on those to be used in the main session.

Warm-down

This is just as important, giving your body time to readjust after the stress of exercise, and helping to reduce the chances of stiffness and sore joints the next day.

- Start your warm-down as soon as you stop the main activity.
- Warm down for five minutes.
- Use a gentle version of your warm-up routine to help flush out waste products from the muscles

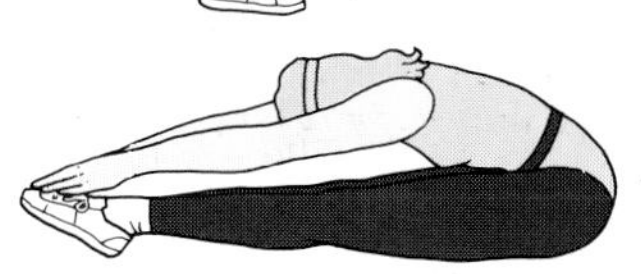

Your training heart rate

Aim to increase your pulse rate gradually during warm-up until it is at the 'training zone' level and then maintain it for the full session. The training heart rate should be between 60% and 85% of the fastest possible rate (220 per minute*), with allowance made for your age.
Work it out like this:

Beginners (220 − your age) × 60%
Fairly fit (220 − your age) × 70%
Very fit (220 − your age) × 85%

Take as an example a 40 year old, fairly fit person:
220 − 40 = 180
180 × 70% = 126
Training heart rate = 126 per minute

***NOTE: DO NOT try to reach 220 per minute – it is DANGEROUS.**

Warm-up Exercises:

Here are some suggested exercises for your warm-up routine. Remember: when doing stretching exercises, stretch out as you breathe out, hold the position for at least six seconds and then repeat three times. Do not bounce into a position. The loosening exercises (numbers 1 and 3) should be done smoothly and without jerks.

1 Windmill arm circling

Swing your arms through their full range of movement, brushing your ear with each swing. Alternate four each arm, then four together, then repeat.

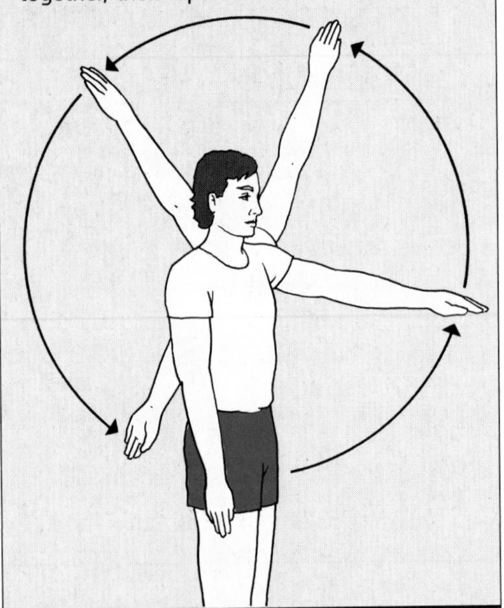

2 Neck stretches

Stand up straight in a comfortable position, legs slightly apart. Look down and touch your chest with your chin. Slowly roll your head round to the left and hold for six seconds, then look down again and repeat looking to the right. Repeat three times in each direction.

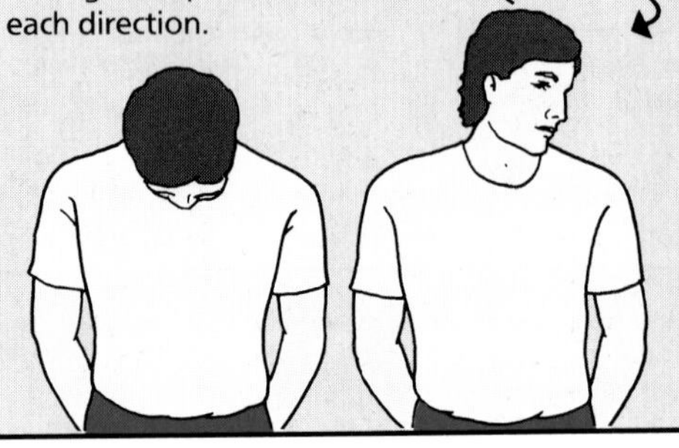

3 Shoulder circles

Again from a standing position, put your hands on your shoulders and circle your shoulders through their whole range of movement (imagine drawing circles with your elbows). Alternate four left, four right, then four together.

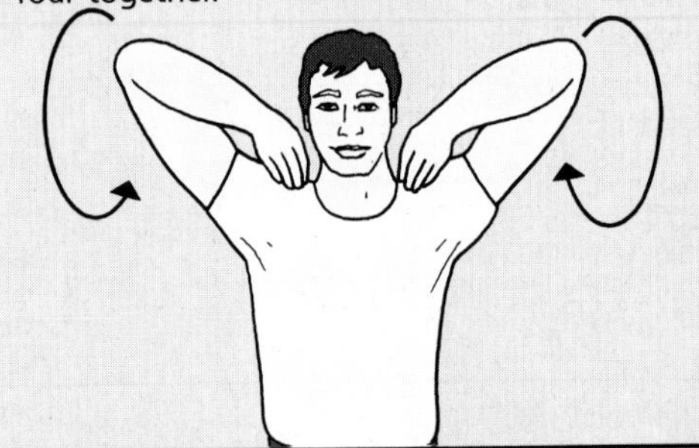

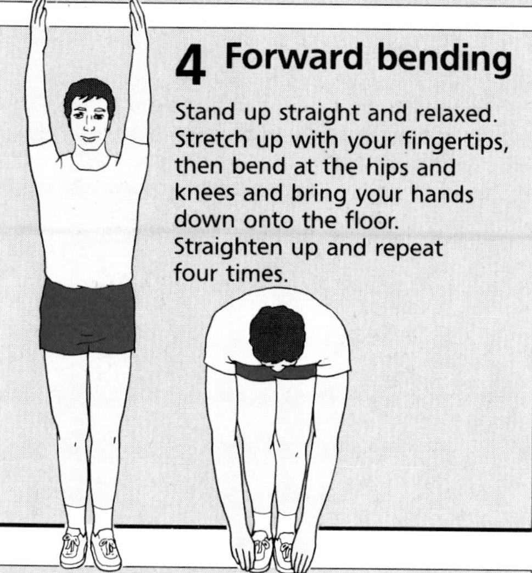

4 Forward bending

Stand up straight and relaxed. Stretch up with your fingertips, then bend at the hips and knees and bring your hands down onto the floor. Straighten up and repeat four times.

5 Side bends

Stand with feet apart and hands on hips. Bend at your hips, first to the left, then to the right. Keep your head at right angles to your body.
Repeat eight times.

6 Trunk turning

Feet apart, reach forwards with your hands at shoulder height. Now turn your head and upper body as far to the left as you can without strain.
Now turn to the right. Keep your legs and hips still throughout.
Repeat eight times.

7 Hamstring stretch

Sit on the floor with your legs together and straight in front of you. Place your hands on your thighs, then slowly stretch down as far towards your ankles as you comfortably can. Hold for six seconds. Return to the upright position and repeat four times.

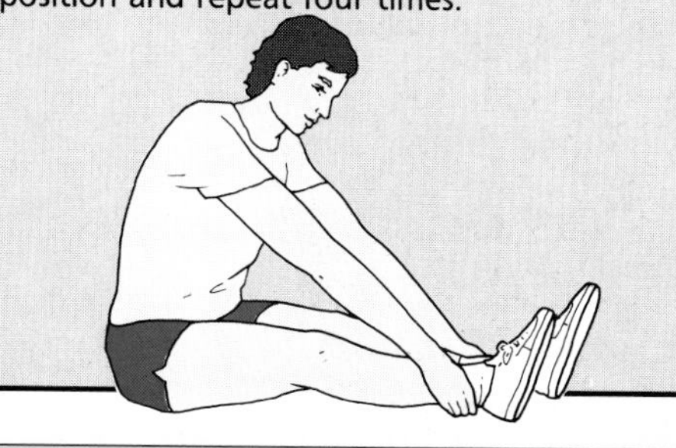

Remember: follow your main exercise session with your warm-down routine, a gentle version of these warm-up exercises (see page 17).

Horses for Courses: Specific Training

Your first aim should be to develop all-round fitness, balancing the elements outlined on pages 10-11, and using the routines and exercises suggested in the following sections. However, some sports obviously require a concentration on suppleness, others on strength, others still on endurance. Most are a combination of all the elements, but with different emphasis on each. So the second stage in your quest for fitness is to adapt your programme so that it is geared specifically to improving your performance in your chosen sport.

Sport	Stamina	Suppleness	Speed	Strength	Concentrate on
Athletics — field throws	4	3	1	2	arms stomach legs
Athletics — track (distance)	1	2	3	4	legs arms
Badminton	3	1	2	4	legs arms
Basketball	1	2	3	4	legs arms
Boxing	1	4	3	2	all muscle groups
Canoeing	1	4	3	2	arms stomach
Cricket	4	2	1	3	legs arms back
Football	1	3	2	4	legs stomach
Golf	4	1	2	3	arms back

The official governing body of your sport should be able to give you detailed advice, but these charts will help you.

They show, in order of priority from 1–4, the comparative requirements of the most popular sports, and specific muscle groups to concentrate on. From this you will be able to work out the proportions of time and energy to spend on each element of your training. Note that these are intended as guidance only, for beginners, and that individual requirements will vary.

Sport	Stamina	Suppleness	Speed	Strength	Concentrate on
Gymnastics	4	1	3	2	all muscle groups
Hockey	1	3	2	4	legs back arms
Ice or roller-skating	1	4	3	2	legs back
Martial arts	2	1	3	4	all muscle groups
Rugby	1	3	4	2	legs shoulders back
Squash	1	2	3	4	arms legs
Swimming	1	2	4	3	arms legs
Tennis	4	1	2	3	arms legs
Volleyball	3	1	2	4	arms legs

Stamina

There are two kinds of stamina (or endurance): aerobic and muscular. Aerobic training is concerned with improving the efficiency of your heart, lungs and circulation (cardiovascular system). Muscular endurance training concentrates on building up the staying power of particular muscles and muscle groups. The two are, of course, related.

AEROBIC TRAINING

Improving your aerobic capacity is desirable whatever sports you play, and particularly vital if plenty of running and prolonged effort are involved. This is probably the single most important element of all-round fitness. Walking, running, swimming, cycling and skipping are all excellent aerobic training activities. Some suggestions for programming walking and running are given here. Alternatively, you can devise your own programme, remembering to build up gradually.

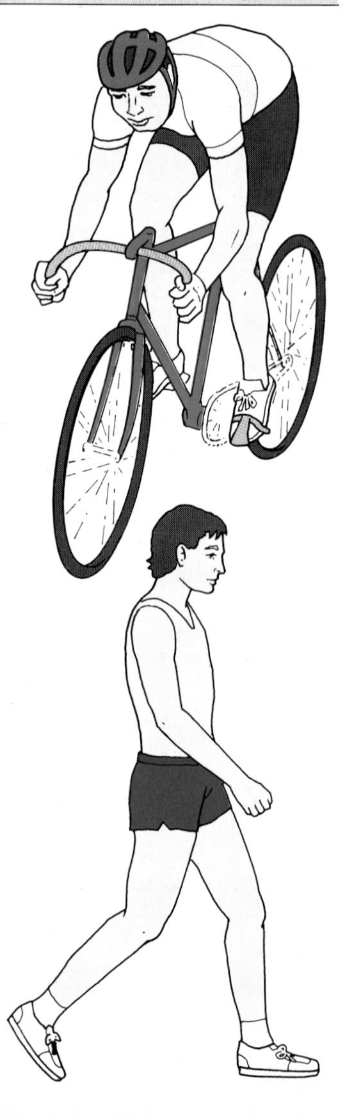

1 Walking

Brisk walking is an excellent introduction to fitness training if you have not exercised much before, and especially if you are older.

- Wear good shoes with socks.
- As with all exercise, build up gradually.
- Use the whole foot, with a smooth heel-to-toe action.

Stage	Frequency	Distance
Month one	Twice per week	1 mile
Month two	Twice per week	2 miles
Month three	Three times per week	2 miles
Month four	Three times per week	3 miles +

2 Running

- Good running shoes are essential (see page 6).
- Find an easy, jogging pace.
- Don't overdo it at first – overuse injuries are not uncommon.
- Intersperse running with walking if you get too tired.
- As you get fitter, you can intersperse short sprints with your jogging (see also varied pace running, below).

Stage	Frequency	Duration
Begin	Twice per week	10 mins
Month two	Twice per week	20 mins
Month three	Three times per week	20 mins
Month four	Three times per week	30 mins

3 Varied pace running

As you become fitter and are able to run for longer, a valuable aerobic workout can be devised using different running speeds. The idea is to intersperse overload situations with appropriate recovery phases. A typical 25 minute session might be:

1. Jogging with 50-yard sprints every 200 yards (5 minutes).
2. Light jogging (2 minutes).
3. Fast, evenly paced run (3 minutes).
4. Brisk walk (2 minutes).
5. Jogging (5 minutes).
6. Evenly paced running with occasional small, acceleration sprints (3 minutes).
7. Brisk walk (2 minutes).
8. Jogging and rhythmical exercises, skipping and gentle knee raises (3 minutes).

Hints

- **Don't forget your warm-up routine before you start.**
- **All the suggested progress charts in this section are for general guidance only – you should be building your pulse rate to its training rate (page 17) and aiming to maintain it for the recommended time, but always stop if you feel fatigued.**

MUSCULAR TRAINING

The most widely used and proven method of increasing muscular endurance – that is, the ability of a muscle or group of muscles to keep up a high level of activity for longer – is circuit training.

Circuit training:

- **Uses body resistance and/or apparatus**
- **Includes a number of different exercises which are performed in turn**
- **Consists of periods of work alternating with rest phases**
- **Should use all the major muscle groups**
- **Should avoid stressing the same muscle groups in consecutive exercises**
- **Can be adapted to include more intense specific activity for any muscles you particularly want to work on**

Here is a typical fitness circuit using a minimum of equipment. Start with a 'work' period of 20 seconds during which you repeat the first exercise as many times as you can. Follow with 30 seconds rest, then go on to the next exercise. As you progress, you can increase each work phase to 60 seconds, followed by 30 seconds rest. The number of repetitions you achieve in each work phase will increase as you get fitter. Keep your movements smooth and controlled.

1 Bench stepping

Step on and off a bench or chair. When both feet are on, make sure your back and legs are straight.

2 Side bends

Hold a medicine ball above your head, arms straight. Then, keeping your arms straight and close to your ears, bend sideways, first to the right, then the left.

3 Skipping

Steady, continuous rope skipping.

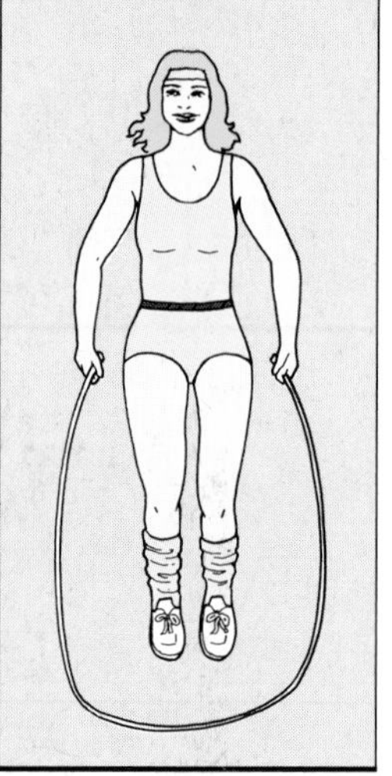

4 Stride jumps on bench

For this you need a low bench or other platform. Stand astride it and jump both feet continuously on and off.

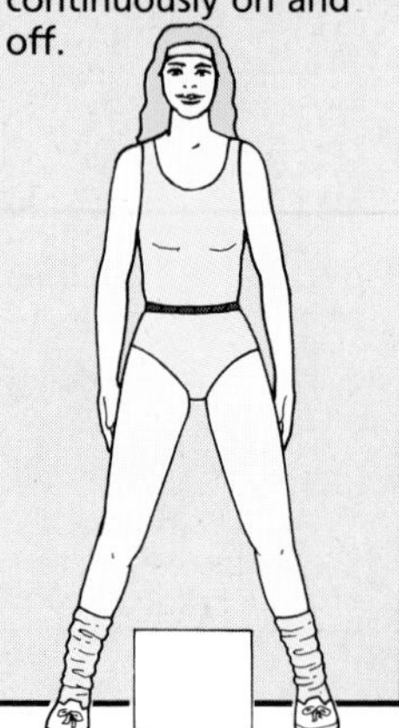

5 Vertical jumps

Kneel on the floor with one leg, fingers touching the floor. Then jump up, changing legs to land in the opposite kneeling position. Your knee should stay just above the floor.

6 Curl-ups

Lie on your back, knees bent, hands on thighs. Lift your head and shoulders off the floor, sliding your hands down your thighs. Return slowly to the starting position. As you progress, try full sit-ups (see page 29).

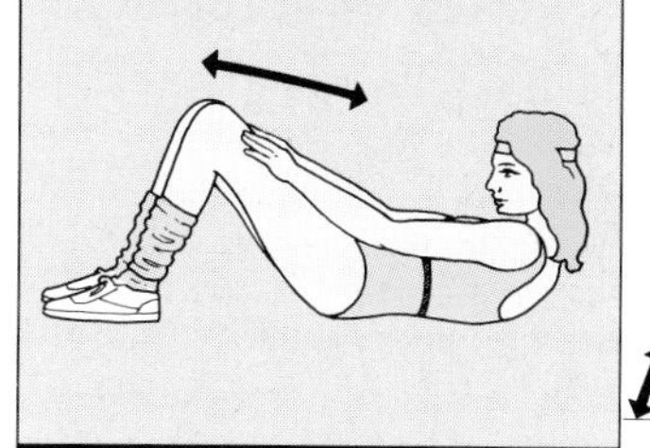

7 Back hyperextension

Lie on the floor on your front, elbows bent and hands under your head. Slowly raise your upper body off the floor. Keep your hips on the floor – don't try to go too far. You may also be able to turn your trunk sideways from the raised position – first left, then right.

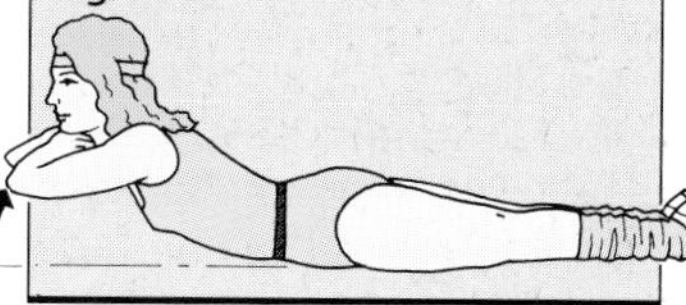

8 Squat thrust

From push-up start position, jump both feet to crouching position, then back again.

9 Kneeling press-ups

Kneel on all fours, with your arms taking most of your weight and shoulder width apart. Now bend your arms to lower your upper body to the floor – don't sag in the middle – and raise yourself back up to the starting position. Repeat. As you get fitter you can progress to the full press-up (see page 28).

10 Shuttle run

Mark two lines about 10 yards apart (if exercising at home, you may have to use a shorter distance). Sprint continuously between them, bending to touch the lines at each end.

Suppleness

Increasing the range of movement in your joints is an important part of the fitness 'mix'. The exercises described for your warm-up routine (pages 18-19) are good for this and you can add the following more advanced stretches to create a routine that uses all the major muscle groups.

Hints

- Don't start until your muscles are thoroughly warmed up.
- Follow your warm-up with ten or fifteen seconds of easy stretching for each exercise.
- Ease, rather than bounce, into each stretch position.
- At maximum stretch you should feel tension but not pain.
- Always do these exercises smoothly and without jerks.
- Relax and breathe calmly and rhythmically.
- Hold each stretch for between 10 and 20 seconds, easing a little further into the position after the first five seconds if you can.
- Do each exercise two or three times at first, building up to five repetitions.

(see also pages 18-19)

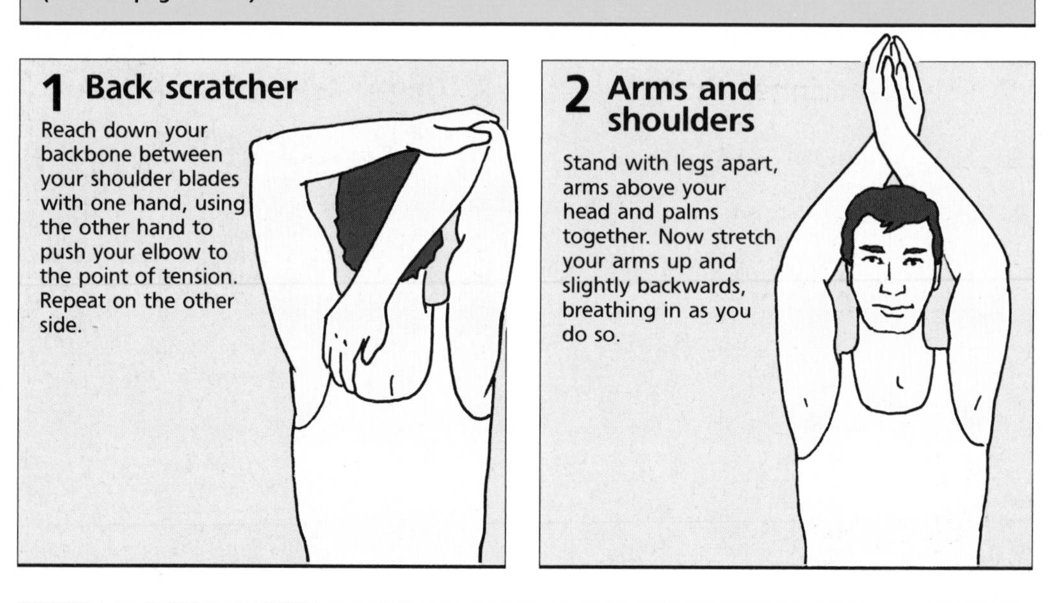

1 Back scratcher

Reach down your backbone between your shoulder blades with one hand, using the other hand to push your elbow to the point of tension. Repeat on the other side.

2 Arms and shoulders

Stand with legs apart, arms above your head and palms together. Now stretch your arms up and slightly backwards, breathing in as you do so.

3 Side stretch

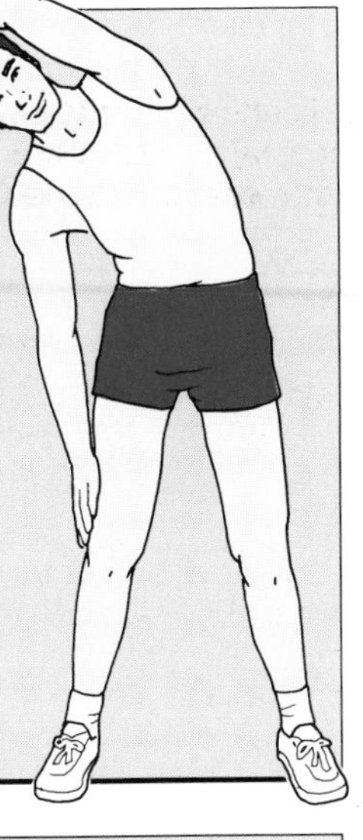

This is an extension of exercise 5 page 19. With feet apart and shoulders back, reach as far down the side of one leg as you can while bringing the opposite arm up and over close to your ear. Don't bend forwards or backwards. Repeat on the other side.

4 Hamstring stretch

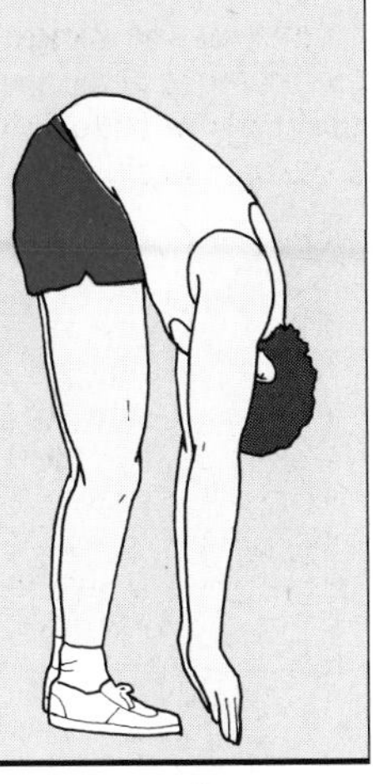

Crouch with your fingertips on the floor and your knees together. Now slowly raise your hips and straighten your knees as much as you can without strain. Keep the weight of your body over your fingertips. For greater effect, press your chin towards your knees as you stretch.

5 Groin and inner thigh stretch

Sit up with your legs as wide apart as they will go, knees locked. Slowly reach forward as far as you can towards a point on the ground midway between your feet.

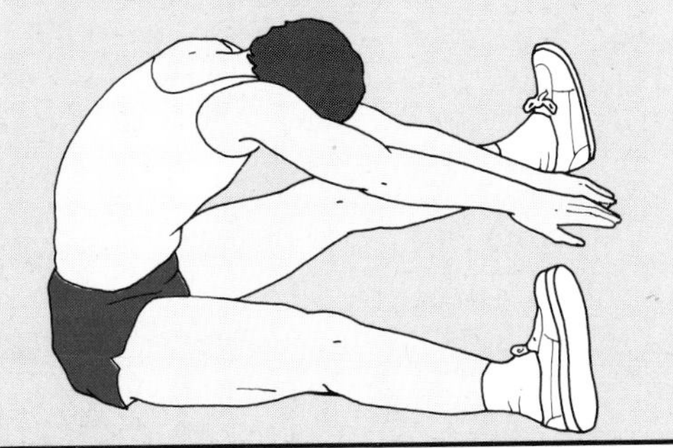

6 Thigh stretch

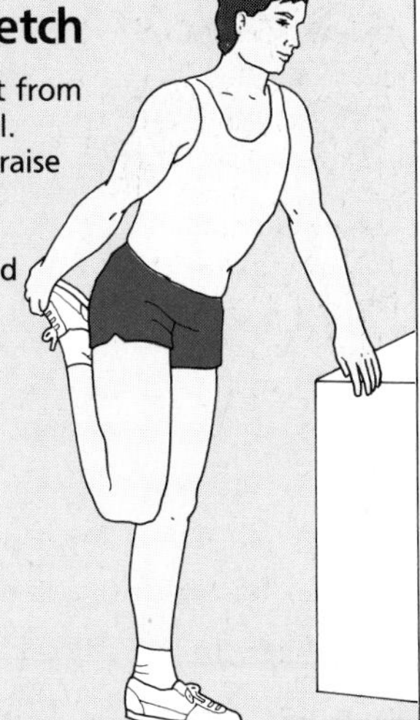

Stand with support from a chair back or wall. Bend one knee to raise your foot behind you, grasping it with your free hand and pulling it up and back. Keep your back straight.

Strength

The exercises in this section are designed to improve your muscle tone, an important element of all-round fitness. More effective exercises for increasing and maintaining strength will be found in the sections on weight training, pages 32-47.

Hints

- **As with all elements of your fitness programme, warm-up properly first.**
- **Don't try to progress too fast.**
- **Start with just a few repetitions of each exercise, building up as you progress.**
- **Keep a record of your progress.**
- **Start by developing your general strength, then adapt the programme to concentrate on areas relevant to your particular sport (see pages 20-21).**
- **Work through the full range of movement.**

1 Press-ups

Adopt the press-up start position, with your arms supporting your body and shoulder-width apart. Bend your arms to lower your chest to the floor, then push up again, keeping your body rigid throughout. NOTE: if these press-ups are too difficult, use the kneeling press-up described on page 25. You could also 'press-up' against a table or chair.

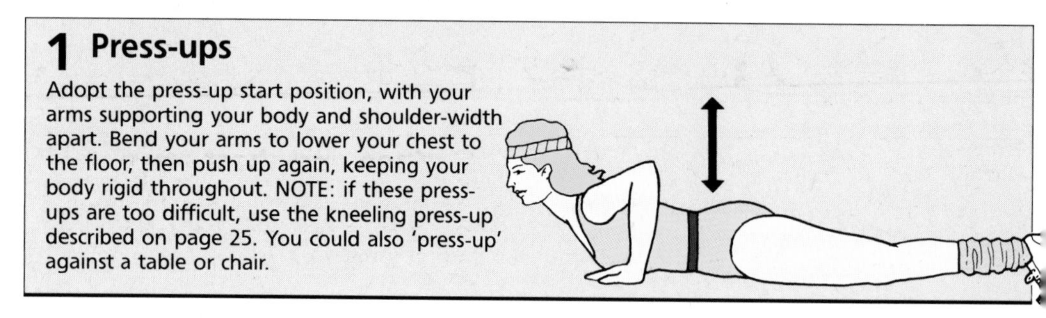

2 Press-up variations (advanced)

a) Starting position as ordinary press-ups, but resting on your fingertips.

b) Starting position as ordinary press-ups but with feet raised.

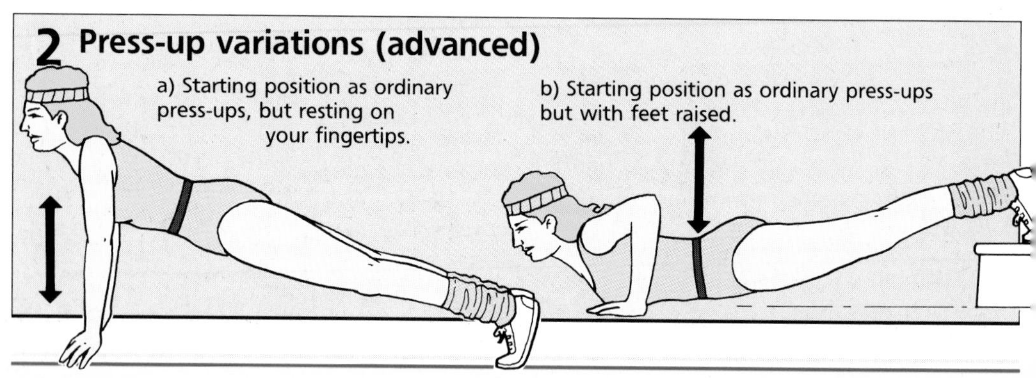

3 Sit-ups

Lie on your back, knees slightly bent and hands resting on your head. Sit up and touch your knees with your elbows. Repeat.

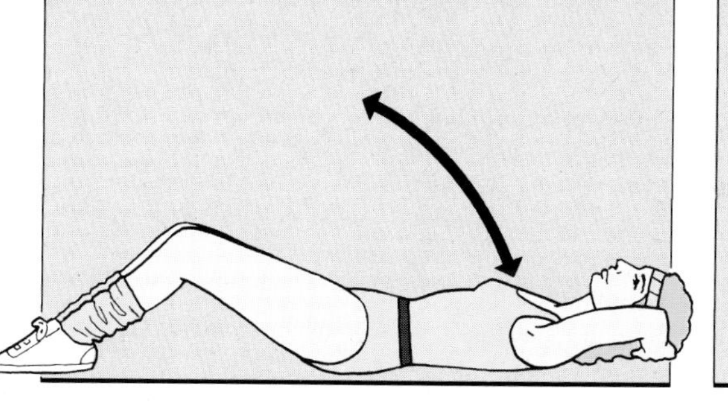

4 Diagonal sit-ups

Starting position as above, but this time when you raise your body, touch your left knee with your right elbow. Lower your body to the starting position and repeat on the other side.

5 Knee raise

Lie on your back, legs outstretched and arms by your sides. Bring your knees up to your chest and then slowly lower your legs again.

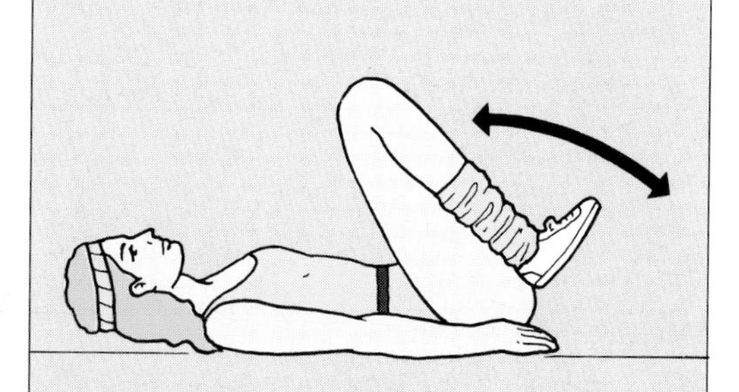

6 Knee and chest raise

Starting position as above, but this time raise your upper body as you bring your knees to your chest. Slowly lower your body and legs again.

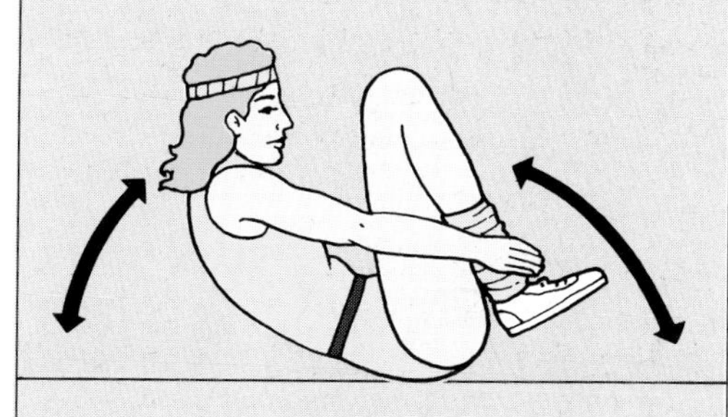

Speed

Speed is a major component of many sports, whether it be overall running speed, speed of limb for a specific activity such as bowling in cricket or serving in tennis, or speed of reaction, as in sprinting, where a fast response to the starter's pistol is of vital importance.

Speed development will be helped by increasing your suppleness, so do spend time on the stretching exercises suggested on pages 26-27. Speed is also, of course, closely related to stamina and strength. The following drills are geared specifically to speed development.

Hints

- **As with all the elements of your training, warm up thoroughly first.**
- **Begin gradually, building up the intensity and duration of the drills as you progress.**
- **Expand and develop the drills as appropriate for your particular sport.**

For these exercises you first need to mark out a 30-yard course on a field or lawn, with markers to indicate the 10- and 20-yard spots. Then perform the drill as follows:

1 Running

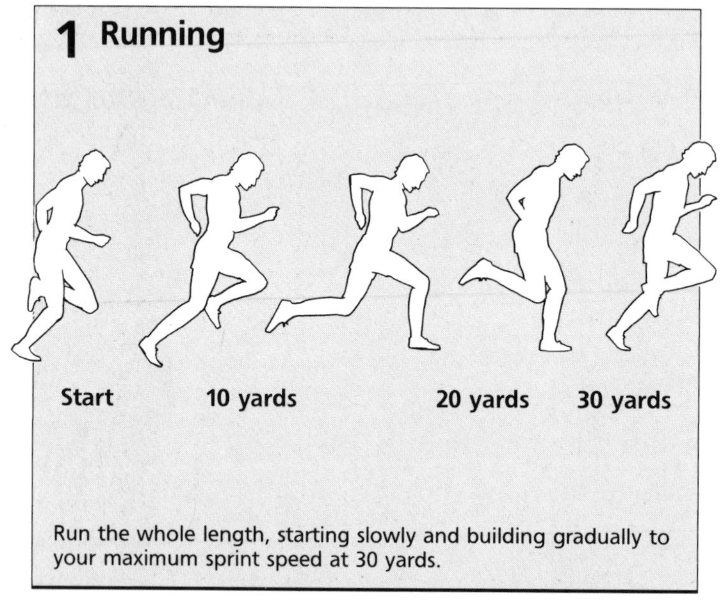

Run the whole length, starting slowly and building gradually to your maximum sprint speed at 30 yards.

2 Jogging

Jog to the 10-yard mark, then accelerate as quickly as you can to maximum speed before the 30-yard mark.

3 Sprinting

Sprint from a standing start for 20 yards.

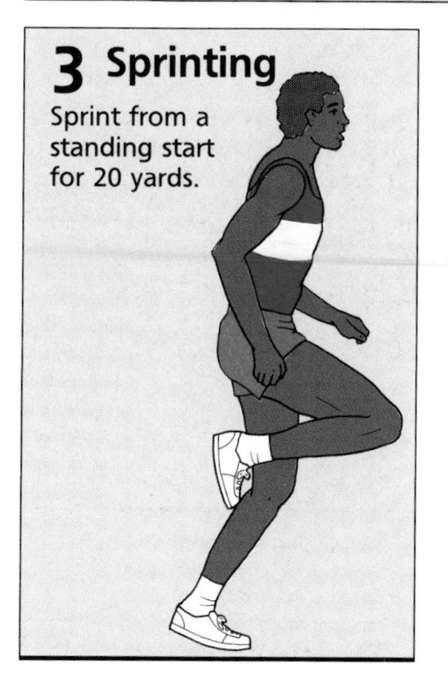

4 High knees drill

Move forward slowly over 20 yards, but bring your knees above waist level in a sprint action. Aim for speed of movement. Repeat three times.

5 Heel kick drill

Kick your heels up keeping your knees low and moving forward slowly over 20 yards. Aim for speed of leg action. Repeat three times.

6 Zig-zag hopping

Hop on your right foot for 30 yards, walk back to the start and repeat for the left foot. Aim to drive high and hard, and try each time to beat your 30 yard record. This is also good for strengthening your ankles.

7 Bounding

Drive high and long in a bounding motion for the full 30 yards. Aim to spend the minimum amount of time in contact with the ground.

8 Speed skipping

Skip at maximum speed for 20-30 seconds.

Weight Training: Before You Start

More and more people, women as well as men, are now using weights, working either with the specialist machines found in gyms and fitness suites or free weights (see pages 47-48). Weight training is not the same as weight lifting, and doesn't mean you will develop bulging biceps – unless that is specifically what you want to do. In fact, working with weights can be used to improve your general fitness, shape and muscle tone as well as your strength and stamina. Weight training is a circuit training method (see page 24).

Which gym?

The number of gyms is increasing all the time, so you are likely to have a choice. It is worth visiting more than one and checking the facilities on offer. A good gym should provide:

- At least ten machines or work stations so that all the major muscle groups can be worked on
- Space for warm-up exercises
- An exercise bike for warm-up
- Well-lit, well-ventilated surroundings
- Trained instruction on first visit and access to advice on subsequent visits
- Wall-charts explaining the different machines and exercises
- Good shower and changing facilities
- Drinks available – preferably a drinking water fountain

Which machines?

There are many different weight-training machines on the market, but although they vary in design and method of use, they will be working your muscles in similar ways. The following pages show simplified versions of some of the more common types of machines. Make sure you choose at least one machine or work station for each main part of your body: chest, shoulders, back, arms, upper legs, lower legs, abdomen.

Which exercises?

The following pages describe 'core exercises' for each major muscle group. These should form the basis of your training session and are important for all-round fitness development, whatever your sport. Next to these, you will find briefer descriptions of additional exercises for the same muscle groups, together with a list of the specific sports for which they are particularly useful.

How much weight?

For each exercise, the amount of weight you use, and the number of repetitions you do, will depend on what you want to gain from the work-out. Detailed advice is given on pages 34-35.

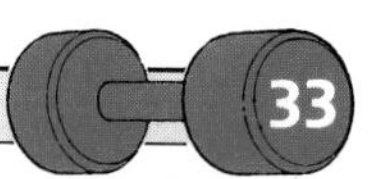

How many repetitions?

Each exercise is repeated a number of times according to the programme you are following (see page 35). The number of repetitions of each exercise are together known as a set. Your session may include more than one set for some or all of the exercises. You can EITHER complete the second and subsequent sets straight away, with appropriate recovery periods in between sets, OR go on to complete one set of all the exercises in your circuit and then start again for your second sets.

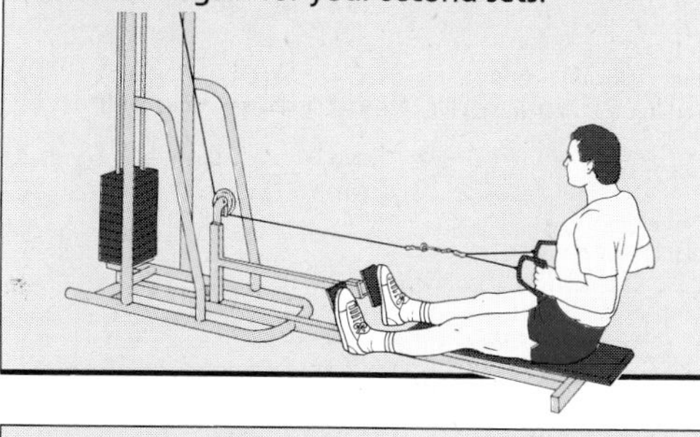

Safety checklist

- **Don't train on your own.**
- **Don't train if you have eaten a large meal or drunk alcohol less than two hours before.**
- **Always warm up properly before you start.**
- **Respect the equipment – the weights are potentially dangerous so follow instructions carefully and never play around in the gym.**
- **Always wear appropriate clothing, paying particular attention to your footwear, which must have non-slip soles.**
- **Keep your breathing regular when exercising – never hold your breath. As a general rule, BREATHE IN just before you start and BREATHE OUT as you move the weight. When exercising at speed, just concentrate on keeping your breathing smooth and even.**

A typical session

As a general guide only, a typical work-out with weights will be devised like this:

Warm-up	**5 minutes exercise bike. 5 minutes minimum stretching exercises.**
Core exercises circuit	**Time taken can vary according to number of sets and repetitions (see pages 34-35).**
Additional exercises	**Select 4-6, but do not do two consecutive exercises on any one muscle group.**
Warm-down	**3 minutes gentle cycling on exercise bike. 2 minutes gentle stretching.**

Weight Training: Charting Your Progress

Step one: define your objectives

Before you start your training, you need to decide exactly what you want to achieve. You can devise a course to improve your stamina, strength or speed, or a combination of any of these. You can also train for body-building (size). Depending on your objectives, several elements of your course will vary:

- Number of exercises
- Weight used
- Speed of exercise
- Rest between sets
- Exercises per muscle group
- Number of repetitions
- Number of sets of each exercise
- Number of sessions per week

The chart on the opposite page will show you how to plan your sessions in detail, taking these variables into account.

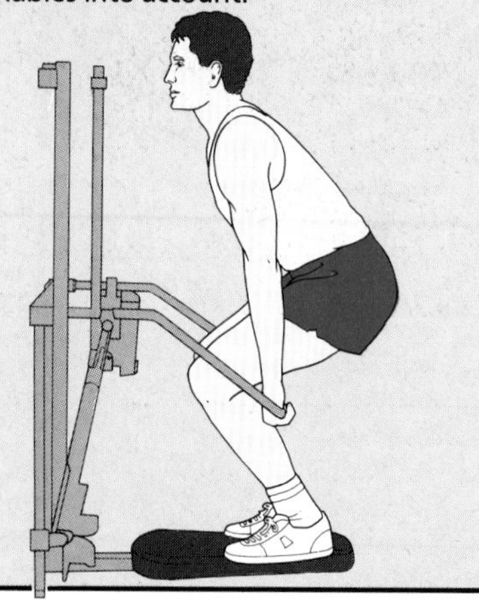

Step two: find your maximum lifting weight

Whatever your objectives, you first need to find the maximum weight you can lift for one repetition on each of the machines or work stations you will be using. You will be using a percentage of these weights, known as the 'loading', in your actual training.

- Follow the instructions for each machine carefully and start with a weight you think will be too heavy for you.
- Do not strain to lift it if it is obviously too heavy – try the next one down instead.
- If you can lift the first weight you tried easily, try the next one.
- Your maximum lifting weight is the one you can comfortably lift for one repetition. Make a note of it for each machine.

Now use the chart on the opposite page to devise your training sessions.

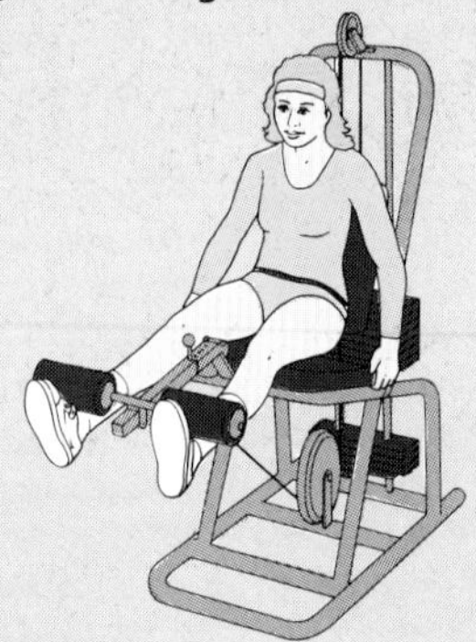

Note: Reassess your maximum lifting weight at least once a month and adjust the weights you are using accordingly.

Your objective	Loading (% of your maximum)	Number of exercises	Exercises per muscle group	Repetitions	Sets	Rest between work stations	Rest between sets	Sessions per week	Speed of exercise
Stamina (aerobic)	20–30%	10 core exercises	1–2	Begin 15 Progress 30	Begin 1 Progress 3	15 secs	1 min	2–4	Fast
Stamina (muscular)	40–50%	10 core plus specific	2–4	Begin 10 Progress 15	Begin 2 Progress 3	30 secs	1–2 mins	2–4	Fast
Strength	60–80%	10 core plus specific	1–2	Begin 6 Progress 10	Begin 1 Progress 3	30 secs+	1–2 mins	2–3	Medium
Speed	60–70%	10 core plus specific	1–2	Begin 6 Progress 10	Begin 2 Progress 5	45 secs+	1–2 mins+	2–4	Fast
Size (body-building)	80%+	20–30	3–6	Begin 4 Progress 6	Begin 2 Progress 5	45 secs+	1–2 mins+	2–3	Slow

On pages 36–46 ten core exercises – one for each major muscle group – are explained, plus additional exercises to build up specific muscles. You should use this chart together with the chart on page 20–21, showing which muscles to concentrate on for a particular sport, to devise a weight training programme that will suit your own needs. (See also A Typical Session, page 33).

Weight Training: The Exercises

Ten core exercises suitable for general fitness training plus additional exercises specific to certain muscle groups are shown here. For further guidance, see charts on pages 20–21 and 35. NOTE: Because machines vary, detailed instructions have not been given. Techniques for using the equipment will be explained at your gym: follow the instructions very carefully.

1 CHEST

Core exercise

Bench press

Note: This exercise is sometimes done on an upright chest press not to be confused with a deltoid machine (see page 42).

- Select required weight.
- Follow the instructions for positioning yourself on the bench.
- Do the required number of repetitions smoothly.

Main effect on:
pectorals
Also benefits
deltoids triceps

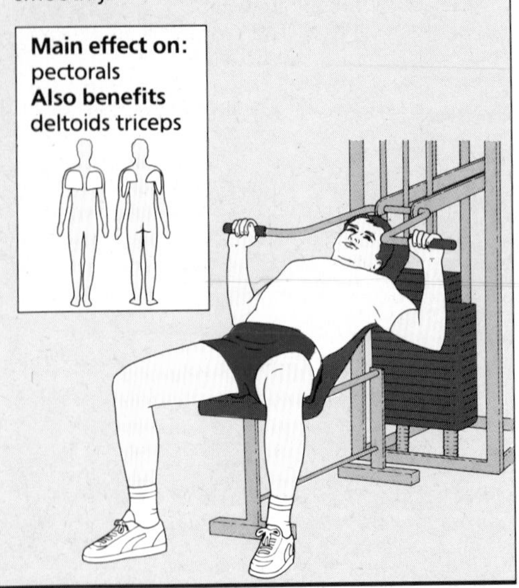

Additional exercise

Pec-deck

Good for:
- athletics (field throws) • badminton
- boxing • canoeing • climbing • cricket
- gymnastics • martial arts • rugby • squash
- swimming • tennis • volleyball

Main effect on:
pectorals

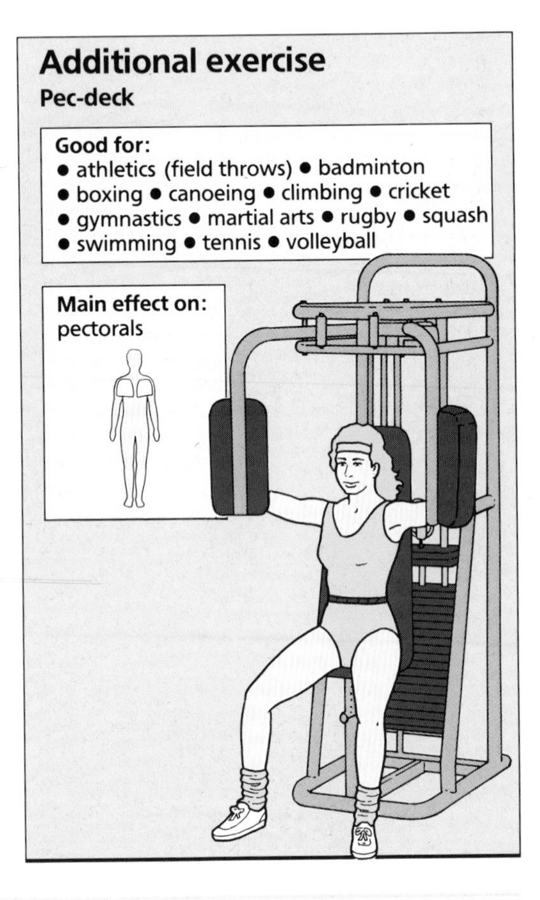

2 BACK

Core exercise

Lateral pulldown

NOTE: some machines do not have seats, and are used in a kneeling position instead.

- Adjust the height of the knee pads, if appropriate.
- Select your required weight.
- Grasp the bar and breathe in.
- Breathe out as you pull the bar down to just above the nape of your neck.
- Return the bar to its original position SLOWLY.

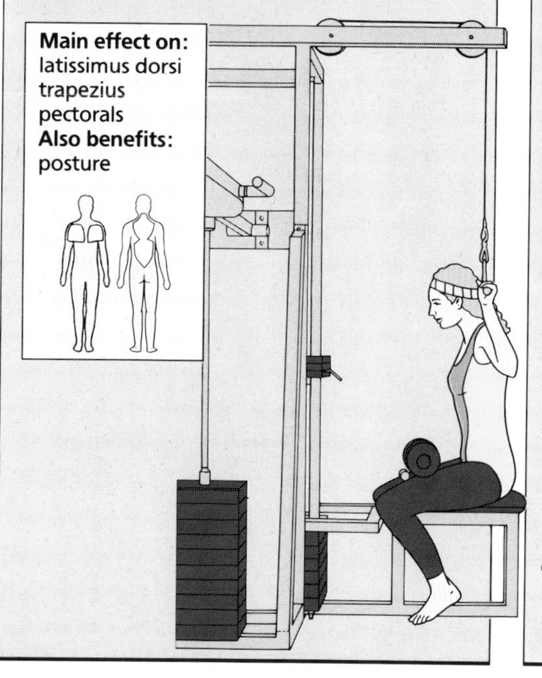

Additional exercise

Seated rowing

Good for:
● athletics (field throws) ● basketball ● badminton ● boxing ● canoeing ● climbing ● cricket ● golf ● gymnastics ● hockey ● handball ● martial arts ● rugby ● skiing ● squash ● swimming ● tennis ● volleyball

Rowing machines come in different designs, for sitting, standing or lying. Seated rowing is particularly good for isolating your upper back muscles. These rowing (or pulley) machines are also often used for leg exercises, replacing the handle/bar with an ankle strap (see pages 39 and 41).

- Select your required weight.
- Follow the instructions for the machine you are using.

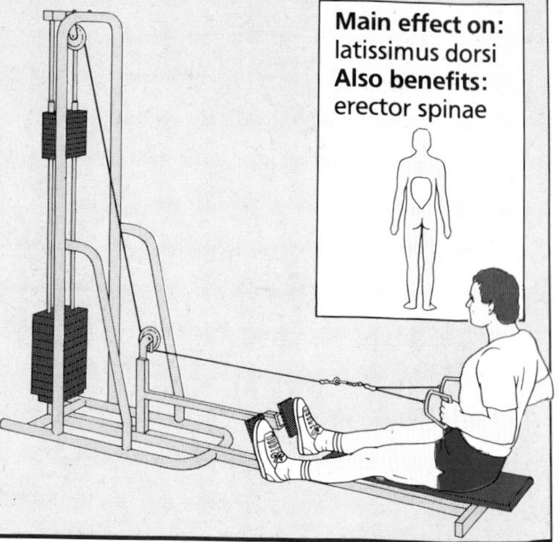

3 LEGS: FRONT THIGHS

Core exercise

Seated leg press

Different types of leg press machines are available: some have curved backs, some involve an almost prone position. All will have an adjustable seat: follow the instructions carefully.

- Select your weight.
- Position yourself as instructed.
- Put both feet on the footplate and push against the weight, extending your legs until your knees are locked.
- As with all exercises, it is important to return the weight to its starting position slowly and with control.

Main effect on:
quadriceps
hamstrings
gluteals
Also benefits:
firming and toning the whole of your upper leg and hip area

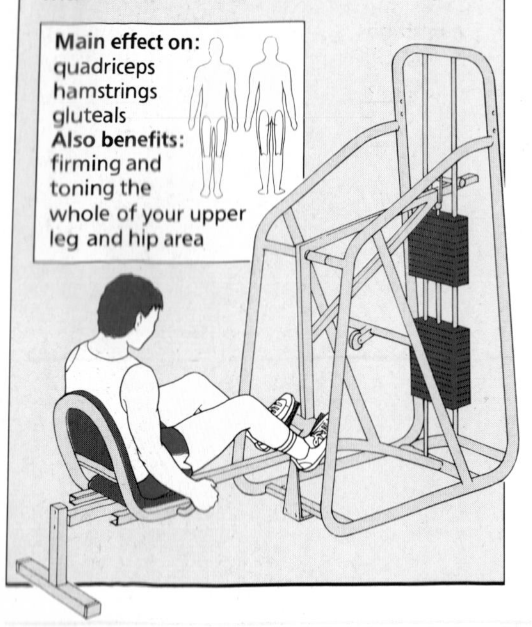

Additional exercise

Leg extension

Good for:
- athletics (track events and jumps)
- cricket ● football ● gymnastics
- hockey ● rugby ● skiing ● skating
- swimming ● volleyball

Some machines have an adjustable seat: follow the instructions carefully.

Main effect on:
quadriceps
Also benefits:
abdominals

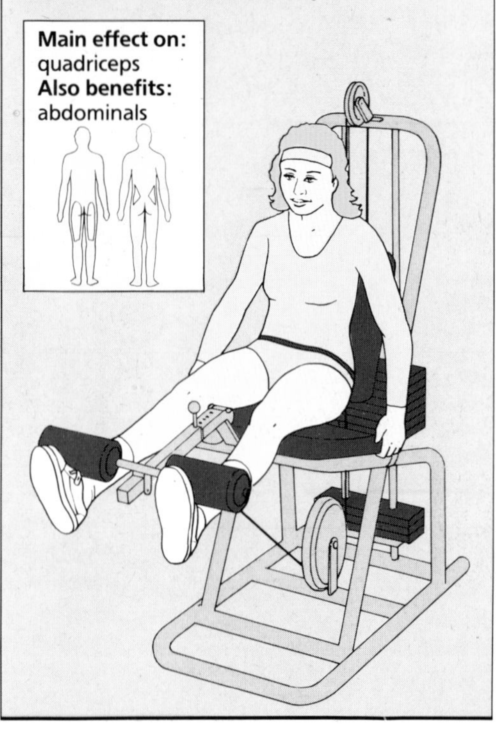

4 LEGS: BACK THIGHS

Core exercise

Hamstring curls

Hamstring curl machines all involve lying on your front and pulling the weight up with your legs, using a cushioned pad at your ankles. Some machines have an angled bench to isolate the muscles even more accurately and avoid pressure on your lower back.

Main effect on:
hamstrings
gluteals

Additional exercise

Hip and back extension

Good for:
- athletics (track events and jumping)
- football • gymnastics • riding • rugby
- skating • skiing • swimming

Not all gyms will have an extensor machine like this one; if your gym does have it, it is also very good for adductor and abductor exercises (see page 41). A low pulley such as that illustrated on page 37 (for the seated rowing exercise) can be used for hip extension by replacing the handle with an ankle strap.

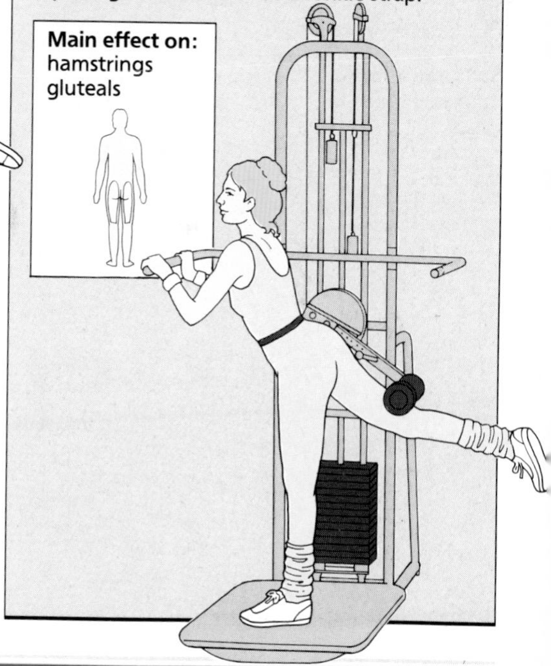

5 LEGS: LOWER LEGS

Core exercise

Calf raise

This machine effectively isolates the calf muscles. NOTE: Some machines do not have seats and use shoulder pads instead of knee pads to pre-load your calves.

- Follow the instructions for height adjustment for the machine you are using.
- Select the required weight.

Main effect on:
gastrocnemius
soleus
Also benefits:
Achilles tendon, strengthening the attachment of the gastrocnemius to the heel

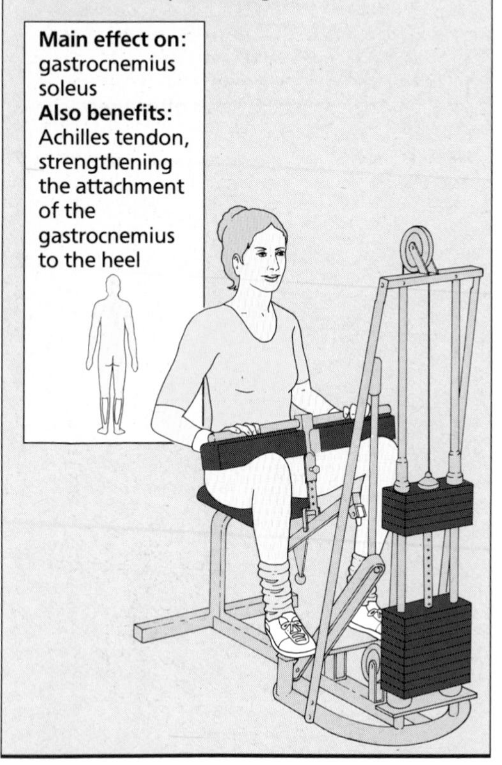

Additional exercise

Toe press

Good for:
● athletics (track events, field throws and jumps) ● basketball ● badminton ● climbing ● football ● hockey ● handball ● rugby ● skiing ● skating ● squash ● tennis ● volleyball

Use the seated leg press machine for this exercise. Extend your legs in the same way onto the foot plate, but this time flex your feet back and use just your toes and feet, not your leg muscles, to push the weight.
NOTE: It is important to have this exercise demonstrated to you by a trained instructor because it is easy for your foot to slip and cause injury.

Main effect on:
gastrocnemius
soleus
Achilles tendon
Also benefits:
ankle joint flexibility

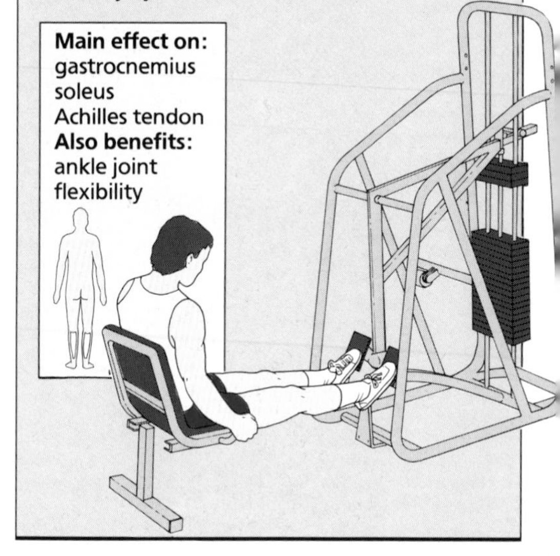

Additional leg exercises

1. Adductor

Good for:
- athletics (track events, field throws, jumps)
- basketball • badminton • climbing
- cricket • fencing • football • gymnastics
- hockey • handball • martial arts • riding
- rugby (backs) • skiing • skating • squash
- swimming • tennis • volleyball

This machine is excellent for isolating the muscles of the inner thigh. You may find a machine which requires a sitting position instead; many gyms use a low pulley machine (see page 37) for this exercise and the abductor exercises described opposite, substituting an ankle strap for the handle/bar.

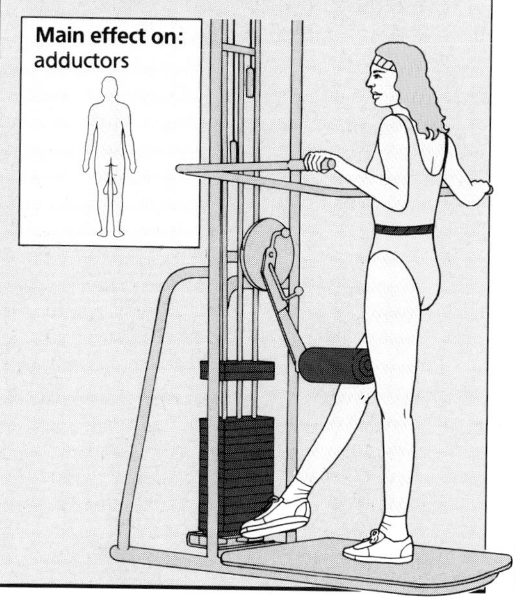

2. Abductor

Good for:
- athletics (track events, field throws, jumps)
- basketball • badminton • climbing
- cricket • fencing • football • gymnastics
- hockey • handball • martial arts • riding
- rugby (backs) • skiing • skating • squash
- swimming • tennis • volleyball

This is for the outer thighs. It works on the same principle as the adductor exercise except that here you are pushing your legs apart against the weight instead of bringing them together. Again, a low pulley is often used.

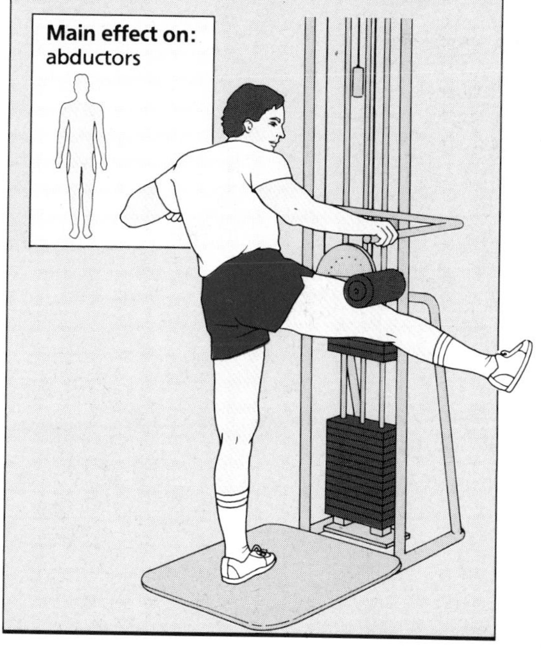

6 SHOULDERS

Core exercise

Upright rows

This exercise is performed using a low pulley machine from a standing position. Your posture and movements are critical to the effectiveness of the exercise, so follow the instructions very carefully. You may also see a deltoid machine which uses a seated position and is designed to isolate the rear shoulder muscles most effectively: here you pull the weights back with your arms at or above shoulder level.

Main effect on:
deltoids
trapezius
Also benefits:
triceps

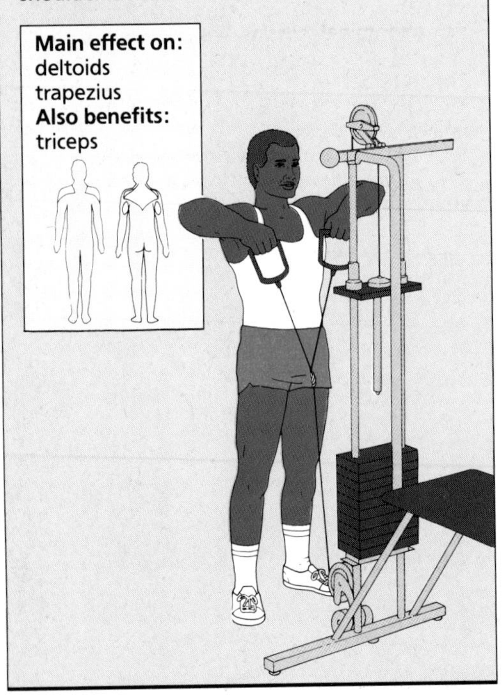

Additional exercise

Shoulder press

Good for:
- athletics (field throws) • badminton • basketball • boxing • climbing • fencing • gymnastics • handball • martial arts • rugby • skating • squash • swimming • tennis • volleyball

This is very effective for exercising the front deltoids. Most machines will have an adjustable seat: follow the instructions carefully, and sit up straight or you could strain your back.

Main effect on:
deltoids
Also benefits:
triceps

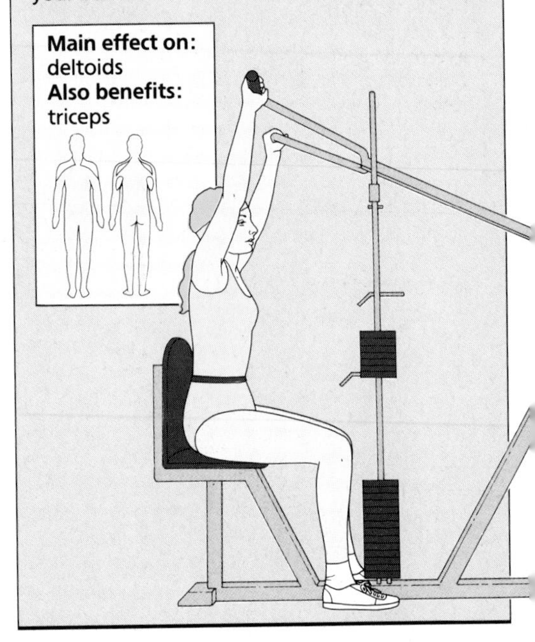

7 ABDOMEN AND TRUNK

Core exercise

Sit-ups

Basic sit-ups were described on page 29 but using the equipment at the gym allows you to include variations in your routine by adjusting the angle of the abdominal board. You may also see an abdominal machine which works on the same principle as sit-ups but allows you to adjust the weight.

- Bend your knees slightly to avoid injury to your lower back.
- As a variation, you can add a twist to your sit-ups (see page 29).

Main effect on:
abdominals
external obliques
(twist sit-ups)

Additional exercise

Side bending

Good for:
- athletics (track events, field throws, jumps)
- badminton • basketball • boxing
- canoeing • climbing • cricket • fencing
- football • golf • gymnastics • hockey
- handball • martial arts • rugby • skiing
- skating • squash • swimming • tennis
- volleyball

You can use the low pulley for exercising the side abdominal muscles.

- Stand upright, feet apart, at right angles to the machine.
- Keep one hand by your side and hold the pulley in the other.
- Bend to the side away from the pulley.
- Keep your back straight and don't move your hips.

Main effect on:
side abdominals

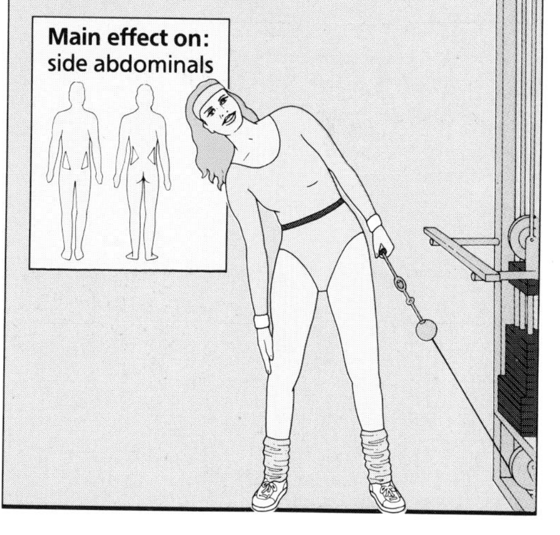

8 ARMS: UPPER ARM FRONT

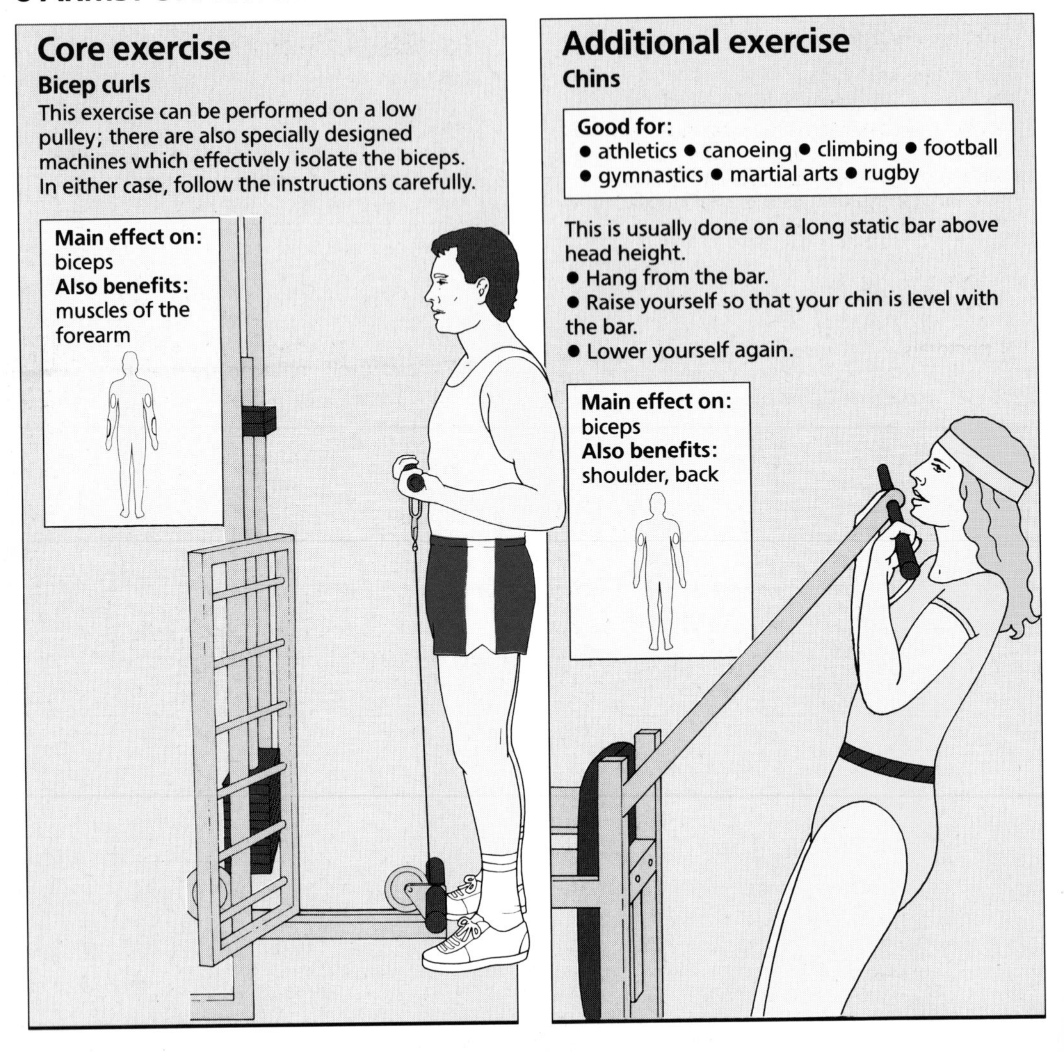

Core exercise

Bicep curls

This exercise can be performed on a low pulley; there are also specially designed machines which effectively isolate the biceps. In either case, follow the instructions carefully.

Main effect on:
biceps
Also benefits:
muscles of the forearm

Additional exercise

Chins

Good for:
● athletics ● canoeing ● climbing ● football ● gymnastics ● martial arts ● rugby

This is usually done on a long static bar above head height.

- Hang from the bar.
- Raise yourself so that your chin is level with the bar.
- Lower yourself again.

Main effect on:
biceps
Also benefits:
shoulder, back

9 ARMS: UPPER ARM BACK

Core exercise

Tricep push down

It is very important to balance any bicep training with exercises for your triceps. These exercises are usually performed on a high pulley machine, though there are some specially designed machines which isolate your triceps.

Main effect on:
triceps
Also benefits:
pectorals

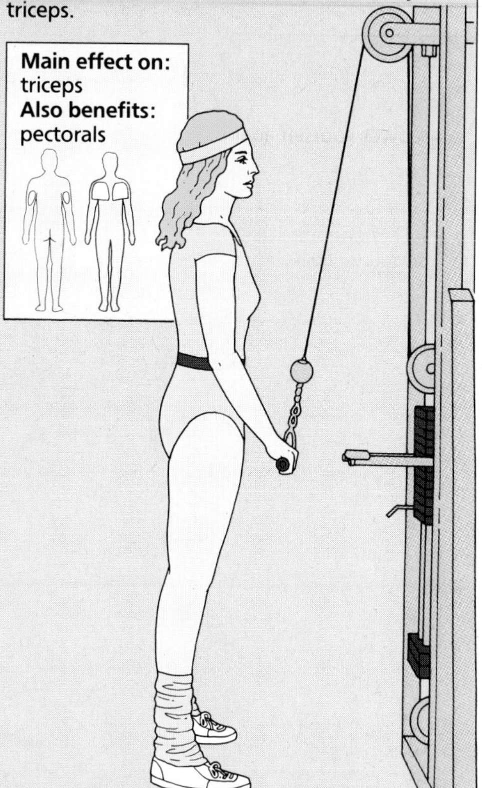

Additional exercise

Dips

Good for:
• athletics • boxing • canoeing • climbing • cricket • fencing • football • gymnastics • hockey • martial arts • rugby

Usually performed on chest high parallel bars.

- Hold each bar with arms locked.
- Lift legs off the ground and bend them behind you.
- Lower elbows until they are at 90°.
- Raise yourself until arms are straight again.

Main effect on:
triceps
Also benefits:
shoulders

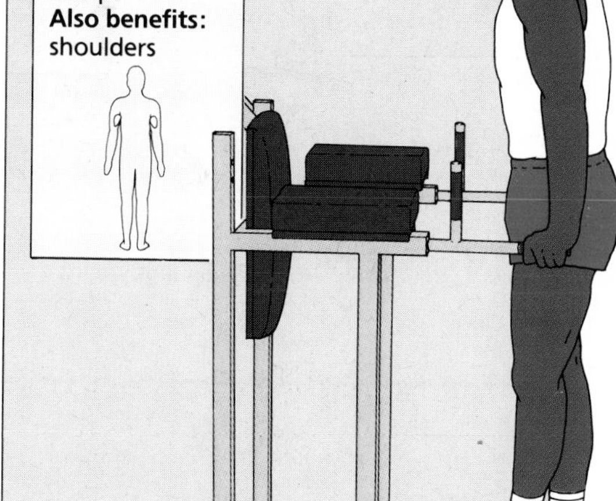

10 ARMS: FOREARMS

Core exercise

Wrist roller

This exercise is performed on a specially designed machine or, sometimes, on a wrist conditioner attachment on a multi-station machine. In either case, the idea is to isolate the wrist and forearm muscles, using an overgrip to roll the bar and wind the weight up with alternate wrist action. Follow the instructions carefully.

Main effect on:
wrist muscles
forearm muscles
Also benefits:
wrist joint flexibility

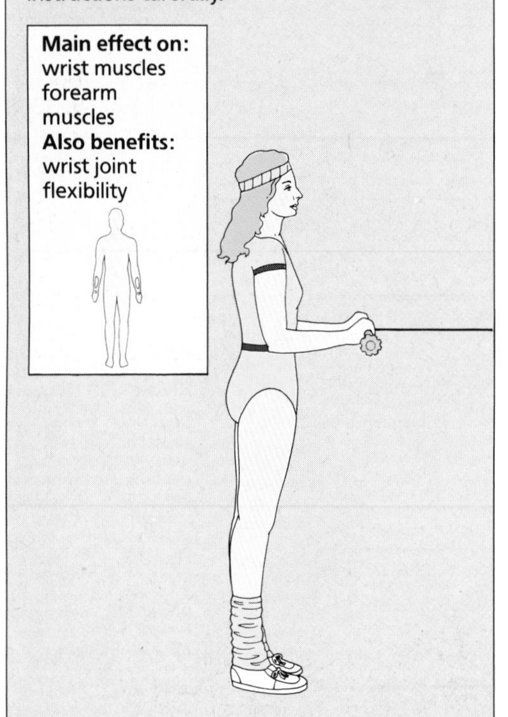

Additional exercise

Wrist curl

Good for:
● athletics (field throws) ● basketball ● badminton ● boxing ● canoeing ● climbing ● cricket ● fencing ● golf ● gymnastics ● handball ● hockey ● martial arts ● rugby ● squash ● tennis ● volleyball

This is the opposite movement for the wrist and is often performed on a low-pulley machine. Here you use an undergrasp, flexing your wrists to move the bar and keeping your arms straight.

Main effect on:
wrist muscles
forearm muscles
Also benefits:
wrist joint flexibility

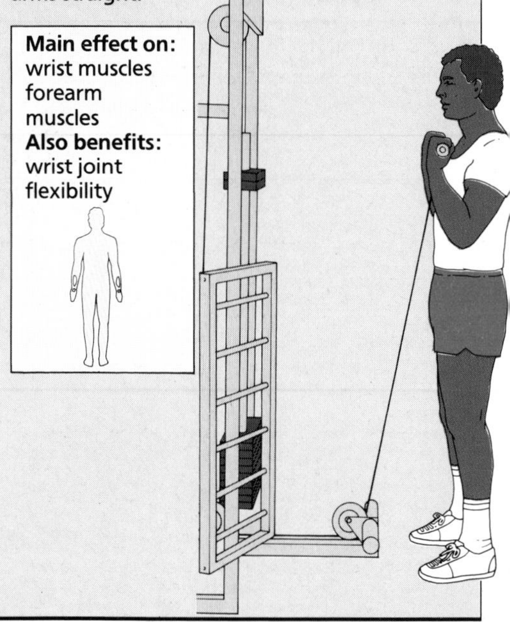

Using Free Weights

Free weights – bar-bells, dumb-bells, wrist and ankle weights – work in a very similar way to the weight-training equipment described in the previous section. They aim to isolate the major muscle groups and subject them to resistance in order to tone, strengthen and, if desired, build them up. Whether you are buying your own free weights or using those at a gym, there should be a good set of charts available which show how to get the best results from the equipment. Do follow the instructions carefully.

The illustrations on pages 47–48 show some of the main exercises you can perform using two types of free weights, dumb-bells and ankle weights. Again, you should aim for a balanced routine, working as many of the major muscle groups as possible., The repetitions suggested are intended as a guide only and represent one set: do more if you are fit enough, less if you are beginning.

For arms, shoulders and chest

Wide grip press

Lie on your back with the weights positioned as shown. Push up, then gently lower the weights. Repeat 10 times, building to 25.

For chest and shoulders

Pull-overs

Lie on your back with just one dumbell held as shown. Bring the weight up and forwards, then slowly return it to the starting position.
Repeat 10 times, building to 25.

For shoulders and legs

Ski swings

Assume starting position as shown, bending both your knees and swinging the weights down past your ankles and then lifting them upwards into the finish position. Repeat 10 times, building to 25. Also a good aerobic exercise.

For shoulders and back

Shoulder and back lifts

Stand with knees slightly bent, weights held out to your sides at shoulder height, palms facing the floor. Now slowly lift your arms up over your head, turning your wrists so that your palms face each other. Slowly return to the starting position. Repeat 10 times, building to 25.

For stomach

Abdominal toner

This exercise uses ankle weights. Lie on the floor with one knee bent and the other leg stretched out. Curl your head, shoulders and chest up off the floor, keeping your back flat. At the same time, lift your straight leg off the floor a little. Return slowly to the starting position without arching your back. Repeat 10 times with each leg.

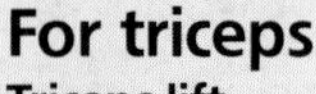

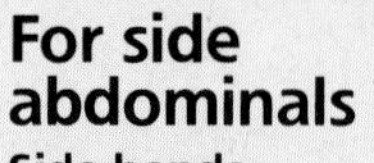

For biceps

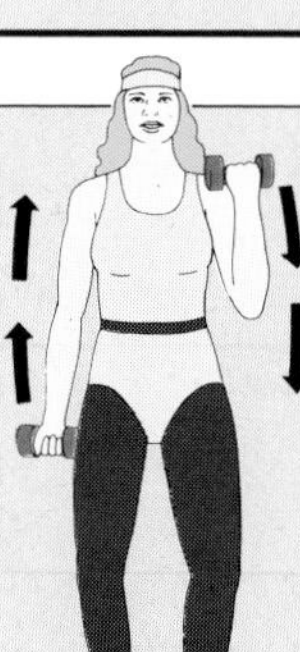

Biceps curl

Stand, feet apart, knees bent, with a dumb-bell in each hand. Your palms should face forward. Keeping your elbows close to your body, bend your left elbow to raise the weight to shoulder height. Lower slowly and repeat with the right arm. Repeat 12 times for each arm, building to 25.

For triceps

Triceps lift

Stand with two dumb-bells held overhead, hands together. Now bend your elbows and lower the weights behind your head. Straighten your arms, then lower again. Repeat 10 times, building to 25.

For side abdominals

Side bends

Start in the first position, then slowly bend as shown. Repeat 10 times, building to 20, for each side.

Printed in Italy